UNITY
SONG SELECTIONS

"REJOICE IN THE LORD
ALWAYS: AGAIN I WILL
SAY, REJOICE."

UNITY SCHOOL OF CHRISTIANITY
LEE'S SUMMIT, MISSOURI
1965

This book is lovingly dedicated to those who in seeking Truth find its uplifting radiance in song.

"Be filled with the Spirit; speaking one to another in psalms and hymns and spiritual songs, singing and making melody with your heart to the Lord."

Unity Song Selections

Revised Edition

1   Praise God that Good is everywhere

MURRAY   DOXOLOGY   GENEVAN PSALTER

Praise God that Good is ev - 'ry-where; Praise to the Love we all may share,

The Life that thrills in you and me; Praise to the Truth that sets us free.

2   All hail the power of Jesus' name

EDWARD PERRONET   Alt.   OLIVER HOLDEN

1. All hail the pow'r of Je - sus' name, Let all men heed the call: Bring
2. Let ev - 'ry kin - dred, ev - 'ry tribe, On this ter - res - trial ball, To

forth our gifts of love and praise, And crown Him Lord of all; Bring
Him all maj - es - ty as - cribe, And crown Him Lord of all; To

forth our gifts of love and praise, And crown Him Lord of all.
Him all maj - es - ty as - cribe, And crown Him Lord of all.

3   God is love; His mercy brightens

JOHN BOWRING

D. E. JONES

1. God is Love; His mer - cy bright-ens All the path in which we rove;
2. Time and change are bus - y ev - er; Earth de - cays, and a - ges move;
3. E'en the hour that dark - est seem-eth Will His changeless good-ness prove;
4. He all earth - ly care un - bind - eth, Rest He send - eth from a - bove,

Bliss He wakes and woe He light - ens; God is wis-dom, God is love.
But His mer - cy wan-eth nev - er; God is wis-dom, God is love.
From the mist His brightness streameth, God is wis-dom, God is love.
Ev - 'ry-where the glo - ry shin - eth, God is wis-dom, God is love. A-men.

4   Hail to the brightness

THOMAS HASTINGS

LOWELL MASON

1. Hail to the bright-ness of Zi - on's glad morn - ing, Joy to the
2. Hail to the bright-ness of Zi - on's glad morn - ing, Long by the
3. Lo! in the des - ert rich flow - ers are spring ing, Streams ev - er
4. See! from all lands, from the isles of the o - cean, Praise to Je -

lands that in dark - ness have lain; Hushed be the ac - cents of
proph - ets of Is - rael fore - told; Hail to the mil - lions from
co - pious are glid - ing a - long; Loud from the mount - ain - top
ho - vah as - cend - ing on high; Fallen are the en - gines of

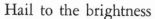

Hail to the brightness

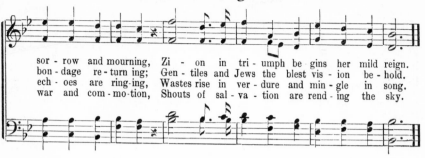

5 Holy, holy, holy, Lord God Almighty

REGINALD HEBER

JOHN B. DYKES

6 None is like God

JOHN BURTON

JOHN B. DYKES

1. None is like God, who reigns a - bove, So great, so pure, so high;
2. In all the earth there is no spot Ex - clud - ed from His care;
3. He is our best and kind - est Friend, And guards us night and day;
4. O if we love Him as we ought, And on His grace re - ly,

None is like God, whose Name is Love, And who is al - ways nigh.
We can - not go where God is not, For He is ev - 'ry - where.
To all our wants He will at - tend, And an - swer when we pray.
We shall be joy - ful at the thought That God is al - ways nigh.

7 How beauteous on the mountains

B. GOUGH

T. R. MATHEWS

1. How beauteous on the mountains, The feet of him that brings, Like streams of liv - ing
2. Lift up thy voice, O watchman! And shout from Zi - on's towers, Thy hal - le - lu - jah
3. Break forth in hymns of glad - ness, O waste Je - ru - sa - lem! Let songs, instead of

foun - tains, Good ti - dings of good things; That pub - lish - eth sal - va - tion, And
cho - rus, —"The vic - to - ry is ours!" The Lord shall build up Zi - on In
sad - ness, Thy ju - bi - lee pro - claim; The Lord, in strength vic - tor - ious, Up -

How beauteous on the mountains

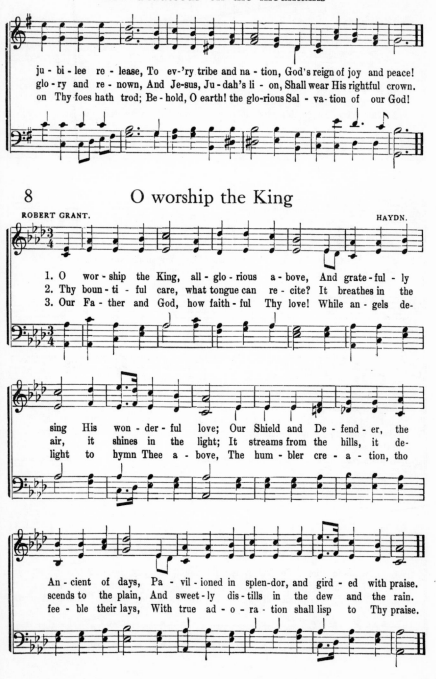

ju - bi - lee re - lease, To ev-'ry tribe and na - tion, God's reign of joy and peace!
glo - ry and re - nown, And Je-sus, Ju - dah's li - on, Shall wear His rightful crown.
on Thy foes hath trod; Be - hold, O earth! the glo-rious Sal - va - tion of our God!

8   O worship the King

ROBERT GRANT.   HAYDN.

1. O   wor - ship the King,   all - glo - rious   a - bove, And grate - ful - ly
2. Thy boun - ti - ful care, what tongue can   re - cite? It   breathes in   the
3. Our Fa - ther and God, how faith - ful Thy love! While an - gels de-

sing His   won - der - ful   love; Our Shield and De - fend - er, the
air,   it   shines in   the   light; It streams from the hills, it de-
light   to   hymn Thee a - bove, The hum - bler cre - a - tion, tho

An - cient of days, Pa - vil - ioned in splen-dor, and gird - ed with praise.
scends to   the plain, And sweet - ly dis - tills in   the dew and the rain.
fee - ble their lays, With true ad - o - ra - tion shall lisp to Thy praise.

9 Love of Jesus, All Divine

F. BOTTOME.   J. B. CALKIN.

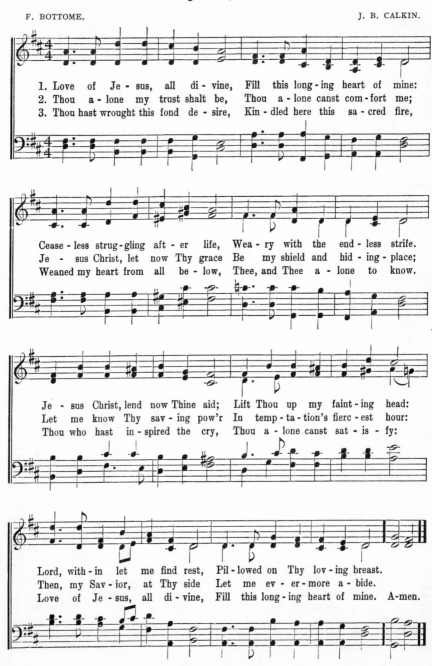

1. Love of Je - sus, all di - vine, Fill this long - ing heart of mine:
2. Thou a - lone my trust shalt be, Thou a - lone canst com - fort me;
3. Thou hast wrought this fond de - sire, Kin - dled here this sa - cred fire,

Cease - less strug - gling aft - er life, Wea - ry with the end - less strife.
Je - sus Christ, let now Thy grace Be my shield and hid - ing - place;
Weaned my heart from all be - low, Thee, and Thee a - lone to know.

Je - sus Christ, lend now Thine aid; Lift Thou up my faint - ing head:
Let me know Thy sav - ing pow'r In temp - ta - tion's fierc - est hour:
Thou who hast in - spired the cry, Thou a - lone canst sat - is - fy:

Lord, with - in let me find rest, Pil - lowed on Thy lov - ing breast.
Then, my Sav - ior, at Thy side Let me ev - er - more a - bide.
Love of Je - sus, all di - vine, Fill this long - ing heart of mine. A - men.

10 Blest Be the Tie That Binds

REV. JOHN FAWCETT.

H. G. NAGELI.

1. Blest be the tie that binds Our hearts in Chris-tian love;
2. Be-fore our Fa-ther's throne We pour our ar-dent prayers;
3. We share our mu-tual woes, Our mu-tual bur-dens bear;
4. When we a-sun-der part, It gives us in-ward pain;

The fel-low-ship of kin-dred minds Is like to that a-bove.
Our fears, our hopes, our aims are one, Our com-forts and our cares.
And oft-en for each oth-er flows The sym-pa-thiz-ing tear.
But we shall still be joined in heart, And hope to meet a-gain.

11 Now the Day Is Over

SABINE BARING-GOULD.

JOSEPH BARNBY.

1. Now the day is o-ver, Night is draw-ing nigh,
2. Je-sus, give the wea-ry Calm and sweet re-pose;
3. Grant to lit-tle chil-dren Vi-sions bright of Thee;
4. Thro' the long night-watch-es, May Thine an-gels spread
5. When the morn-ing wak-ens, Then may I a-rise

Shad-ows of the eve-ning Steal a-cross the sky.
With Thy ten-d'rest bless-ing May our eye-lids close.
Guard the sail-ors toss-ing On the deep blue sea.
Their white wings a-bove me, Watch-ing round my bed.
Pure and fresh and sin-less In Thy ho-ly eyes. A-men.

eve-ning Steal a-cross the sky.

12 There is sunshine in my soul today

E. E. HEWITT

JNO. R. SWENEY

1. There is sun-shine in my soul to-day, More glo-ri-ous and bright
2. There is springtime in my soul to-day, For when the Lord is near,
3. There is glad-ness in my soul to-day, And hope, and praise, and love,

Than glows in a-ny earth-ly sky, For Je-sus is my Light.
The dove of peace sings in my heart, The flowers of grace ap-pear,
For bless-ings which He gives me now, For joys laid up a-bove,

REFRAIN

O, there's sun — shine, Bless-ed sun — shine,
sun-shine in my soul, sun-shine in my soul,

While the peace-ful, hap-py mo-ments roll;
hap-py mo-ments roll;

When Je-sus shows His smil-ing face, There is sun-shine in my soul.

13 There is sunshine in my soul today

1 There is sunshine in my soul today,
   It is glorious and bright,
   Ever glowing in its bright'ning ray
   For Jesus is my light.

Chorus.—O there's sunshine, blessed sunshine,
   As the peaceful, happy moments roll;
   For I behold His smiling face
   And there's sunshine in my soul.

2 There is springtime in my soul today.
   I know the Lord is near;
   The notes of peace sing in my heart,
   The joys of grace appear.

3 There is gladness in my soul today,
   And hope, and love, and praise,
   For blessings which He gives me now,
   Have brightened all my days.

14 O Lord of heaven and earth and sea

CHRISTOPHER WORDSWORTH   LOUIS LE SAINT

Alto prominent for four measures.

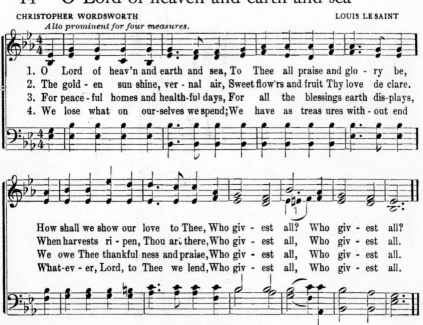

1. O Lord of heav'n and earth and sea, To Thee all praise and glo - ry be,
2. The gold - en sun shine, ver - nal air, Sweet flow'rs and fruit Thy love de clare.
3. For peace - ful homes and health-ful days, For all the blessings earth dis-plays,
4. We lose what on our-selves we spend; We have as treas ures with - out end

How shall we show our love to Thee, Who giv - est all? Who giv - est all?
When harvests ri - pen, Thou art there, Who giv - est all, Who giv - est all.
We owe Thee thankful ness and praise, Who giv - est all, Who giv - est all.
What-ev - er, Lord, to Thee we lend, Who giv - est all, Who giv - est all.

Yes, God is good

E. L. FOLLEN, Alt

LOWELL MASON

1. Yes God is good, in earth and sky, From o - cean depths and spreading wood,
2. The sun that keeps his track-less way, And downward pours his gold - en flood,
3. The mer - ry birds pro-long the strain, Their song with ev - 'ry spring re-newed;
4. Yes, "God is good," all na - ture says, By God's own hand with speech en-dued;

Ten thousand voic-es seem to cry, "God made us all, and God is good!"
Night's sparkling hosts all seem to say, In ac-cents clear, that "God is good."
And balm - y air, and fall-ing rain, Each soft-ly whis-per, "God is good!"
And man, in loud-er notes of praise, Should sing for joy that "God is good." A - men.

Come, Thou almighty King

CHARLES WESLEY

FELICE DE GIARDINI

1. Come, Thou al - might - y King, Help us Thy name to sing,
2. Come, Thou in - car - nate Word, Gird on Thy might - y sword,
3. Come, Ho - ly Com - fort - er, Thy sa - cred wit - ness bear
4. To the great One in Three, E - ter - nal prais - es be

Help us to praise: Fa - ther, all glo - ri - ous, O'er all vic-
Our pray'r at - tend: Come, and Thy peo - ple bless, And give Thy
In this glad hour: Thou who al - might - y art, Now rule in
Hence ev - er - more. His sov - 'reign maj - es - ty May we in

Come, Thou Almighty King

to - ri - ous, Come, and reign o - ver us, An - cient of Days.
word suc - cess; Spir - it of ho - li - ness, On us de - scend.
ev - 'ry heart, And ne'er from us de - part, Spir - it of pow'r.
glo - ry see, And to e - ter - ni - ty Love and a - dore.

17   # We praise Thee, O God

WM. P. MACKAY

JOHN J. HUSBAND

1. We praise Thee, O God, For the Spir - it of light, That has shown us Thy
2. All glo - ry and praise, For Thy like - ness with - in; As the sons of the
3. Re - joice and re - joice! Let the Son in you shine; Give praise and thanks-
4. Re - joice and be glad For the life of to - day; And the prom - ise it

CHORUS

good - ness And scat - tered our night.   Hal - le - lu - jah! Thine the glo - ry; Hal - le -
Fa - ther, Our tri - umphs be - gin.
giv - ing For love that's di - vine.
car - ries: "I'm with you al - way."

lu - jah! a - gain! Hal - le - lu - jah! Thine the glo - ry; We praise Thee. A - men.

18   We hail the dawning of the day

E. A. H.

REV. ELISHA A. HOFFMAN

1. We hail the dawn-ing of the day, For the king-dom of Christ is come;
2. The reign of peace shall be com-plete, For the king-dom of Christ is come;

Where Love and Truth now have full sway, For the king-dom of Christ is come;
The earth shall bow at Je-sus' feet, For the king-dom of Christ is come;

Now to the earth's re-mot-est bound The gos-pel mes-sage does re-sound,
For-ev-er shouts of joy re-sound, For peace and plen-ty shall a-bound,

And peace and sweet good will a-bound, For the king-dom of Christ is come.
And broth-er-hood and love pro-found, For the king-dom of Christ is come.

CHORUS.

For the king - dom is come,....... For the king - dom is
For the king-dom of Christ is ful - ly come, For the king-dom of Christ is

We hail the dawning of the day

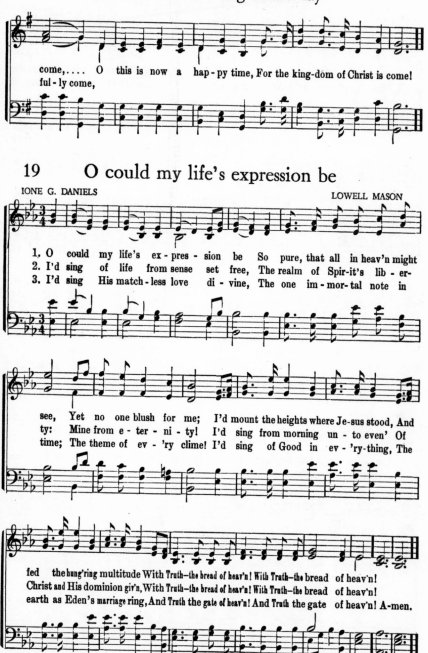

come,.... O this is now a hap-py time, For the king-dom of Christ is come!
ful-ly come,

19   O could my life's expression be

IONE G. DANIELS   LOWELL MASON

1, O could my life's ex - pres - sion be So pure, that all in heav'n might
2. I'd sing of life from sense set free, The realm of Spir-it's lib - er-
3. I'd sing His match-less love di - vine, The one im - mor-tal note in

see, Yet no one blush for me; I'd mount the heights where Je-sus stood, And
ty: Mine from e - ter - ni - ty! I'd sing from morning un - to even' Of
time; The theme of ev - 'ry clime! I'd sing of Good in ev - 'ry-thing, The

fed the hung'ring multitude With Truth—the bread of heav'n! With Truth—the bread of heav'n!
Christ and His dominion giv'n, With Truth—the bread of heav'n! With Truth—the bread of heav'n!
earth as Eden's marriage ring, And Truth the gate of heav'n! And Truth the gate of heav'n! A-men.

20 True-hearted, whole-hearted

FRANCES R. HAVERGAL

GEO. C. STEBBINS

1. True-heart-ed, whole heart ed, faith-ful and loy - al, Kings of our lives, by Thy
2. True-heart-ed, whole-heart-ed, full - est al - le - giance, Yield-ing henceforth to our

grace we will be; Un - der the standard ex-alt - ed and loy - al, Strong in Thy
glo - ri - ous King; Val - iant en - deav - or and loving o - bedience, Free - ly and

CHORUS.

strength we will work now for Thee. Peal out the watchword! si - lence it nev - er!
joy - ous - ly now would we bring. Peal si - lence

Song of our spir-its, re - joic - ing and free; Peal out the watchword!
Song re joic - ing and free; Peal

loy - al for - ev - er, Kings of our lives, by Thy grace we will be.
loy - al Kings

21 Mine eyes have seen the glory

JULIA WARD HOWE

WILLIAM STEFFE

1. Mine eyes have seen the glo - ry of the com - ing of the Lord; He is
2. He has sound-ed forth the trum - pet that shall nev - er call re-treat; He is
3. In the beau-ty of the lil - ies, Christ was born a - cross the sea, With a

trampling out the vin - tage where the grapes of wrath are stored: He hath
sift - ing out the hearts of men be - fore His judg-ment-seat; O, be
glo - ry in His bos - om that trans-fig - ures you and me; As he

loosed the fate-ful lightning of His ter - ri-ble, swift sword! His truth is marching on.
swift, my soul, to answer Him! be ju - bi-lant, my feet! Our God is marching on.
lived to make men ho - ly, let us live to make men free, While God is marching on.

REFRAIN

Glo - ry! glo - ry! Hal - le - lu - jah! Glo - ry! glo - ry! Hal - le - lu - jah!

Glo - ry! glo - ry! Hal - le - lu - jah! His truth is march-ing on.

22 Loved with everlasting Love

WILLIAM F. SHERWIN

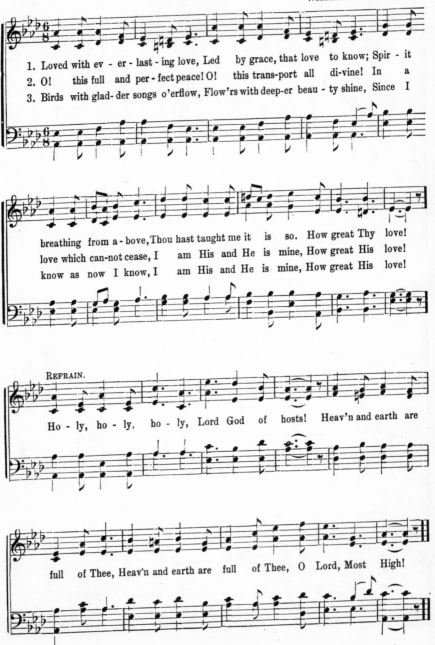

1. Loved with ev-er-last-ing love, Led by grace, that love to know; Spir-it
2. O! this full and per-fect peace! O! this trans-port all di-vine! In a
3. Birds with glad-der songs o'erflow, Flow'rs with deep-er beau-ty shine, Since I

breathing from a-bove, Thou hast taught me it is so. How great Thy love!
love which can-not cease, I am His and He is mine, How great His love!
know as now I know, I am His and He is mine, How great His love!

REFRAIN.

Ho-ly, ho-ly, ho-ly, Lord God of hosts! Heav'n and earth are

full of Thee, Heav'n and earth are full of Thee, O Lord, Most High!

23   The Lord is in His holy temple

W. H. BAGBY, Alt.

J. H. FILLMORE

1. The Lord is in His ho-ly tem-ple; Let earth be-fore Him
2. The Lord is in His ho-ly tem-ple De-clare the Truth in

sil-ence keep. In rev-'rence bow, ye loft-y moun-tains, And
un-i-ty; Be si-lent in His joy-ful pres-ence, Whose

REFRAIN

be Thou still, O won-drous deep! The Lord is in His ho-ly tem-ple;
glo-ry fills e-ter-ni-ty.

The Lord is in His ho-ly tem-ple. Keep si-lence, Keep si-lence,

Keep si-lence be-fore Him.

A - - men.
The Lord is in His ho-ly tem-ple.

24 Living with Jesus

MAJ. D. W. WHITTLE. Alt.

MAY WHITTLE MOODY

1. Liv - ing with Je - sus, by life reck - oned mine; Liv - ing with Je - sus, a
2. Mo - ment by mo - ment, I'm do - ing His will, Prov - ing His prom - is - es

new life di - vine; Look - ing to Je - sus till glo - ry does shine; Mo - ment by
He will ful - fill. This blest as - sur - ance my be - ing does thrill, Je - sus, my

CHORUS

mo - ment, O Lord, I am Thine. Moment by moment, I'm kept in His love;
Sav - iour, a - bides with me still.

Mo - ment by mo - ment, I've life from a - bove; Look - ing to Je - sus till

rit.

glo - ry does shine; Mo - ment by mo - ment, O Lord, I am Thine.

25 Take my life and let it be

FRANCIS R. HAVERGAL

Arr. from CONCONE

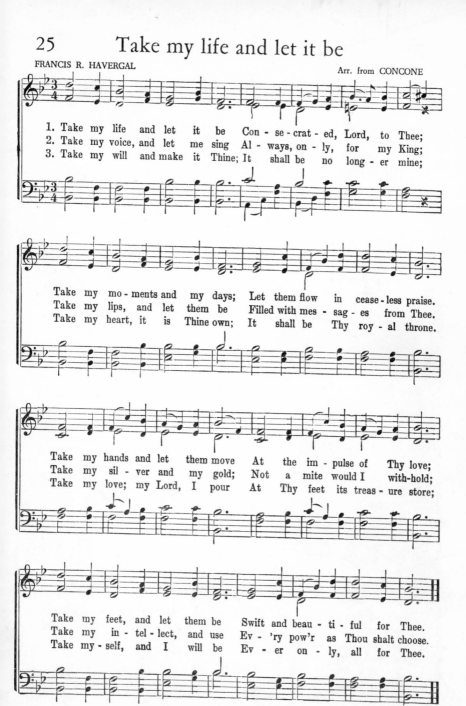

1. Take my life and let it be Con - se - crat - ed, Lord, to Thee;
2. Take my voice, and let me sing Al - ways, on - ly, for my King;
3. Take my will and make it Thine; It shall be no long - er mine;

Take my mo - ments and my days; Let them flow in cease - less praise.
Take my lips, and let them be Filled with mes - sag - es from Thee.
Take my heart, it is Thine own; It shall be Thy roy - al throne.

Take my hands and let them move At the im - pulse of Thy love;
Take my sil - ver and my gold; Not a mite would I with-hold;
Take my love; my Lord, I pour At Thy feet its treas - ure store;

Take my feet, and let them be Swift and beau - ti - ful for Thee.
Take my in - tel - lect, and use Ev - 'ry pow'r as Thou shalt choose.
Take my - self, and I will be Ev - er on - ly, all for Thee.

26 O God, in whom we live and move

SAMUEL LONGFELLOW

BEETHOVEN

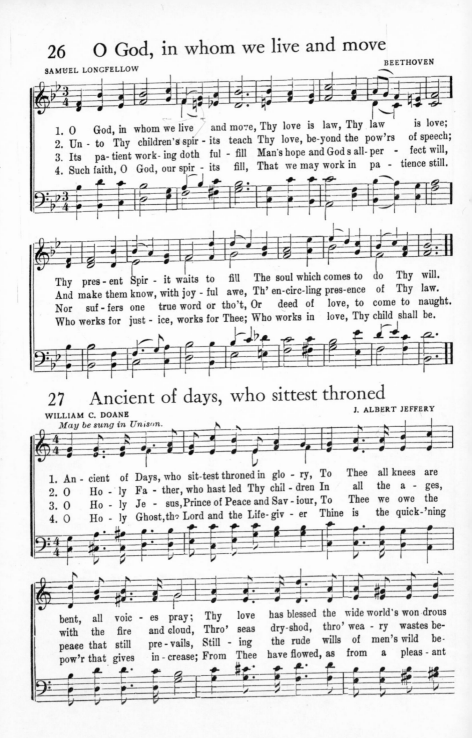

1. O God, in whom we live and move, Thy love is law, Thy law is love;
2. Un-to Thy children's spir-its teach Thy love, be-yond the pow'rs of speech;
3. Its pa-tient work-ing doth ful-fill Man's hope and God's all-per - fect will,
4. Such faith, O God, our spir-its fill, That we may work in pa - tience still.

Thy pres-ent Spir-it waits to fill The soul which comes to do Thy will.
And make them know, with joy-ful awe, Th' en-cir-cling pres-ence of Thy law.
Nor suf-fers one true word or tho't, Or deed of love, to come to naught.
Who works for just-ice, works for Thee; Who works in love, Thy child shall be.

27 Ancient of days, who sittest throned

WILLIAM C. DOANE

J. ALBERT JEFFERY

May be sung in Unison.

1. An-cient of Days, who sit-test throned in glo-ry, To Thee all knees are
2. O Ho-ly Fa-ther, who hast led Thy chil-dren In all the a-ges,
3. O Ho-ly Je-sus, Prince of Peace and Sav-iour, To Thee we owe the
4. O Ho-ly Ghost, the Lord and the Life-giv-er Thine is the quick-'ning

bent, all voic-es pray; Thy love has blessed the wide world's won-drous
with the fire and cloud, Thro' seas dry-shod, thro' wea-ry wastes be-
peace that still pre-vails, Still-ing the rude wills of men's wild be-
pow'r that gives in-crease; From Thee have flowed, as from a pleas-ant

29 He who suns and worlds upholdeth

THOMAS H. GILL

JOHN ZUNDEL

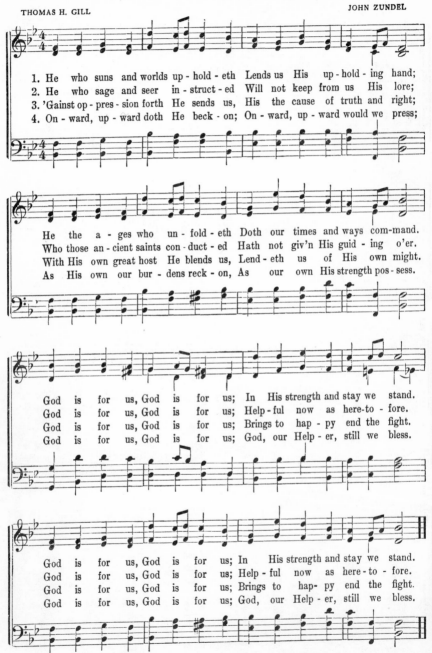

1. He who suns and worlds up - hold - eth Lends us His up - hold - ing hand;
2. He who sage and seer in - struct - ed Will not keep from us His lore;
3. 'Gainst op - pres - sion forth He sends us, His the cause of truth and right;
4. On - ward, up - ward doth He beck - on; On - ward, up - ward would we press;

He the a - ges who un - fold - eth Doth our times and ways com - mand.
Who those an - cient saints con - duct - ed Hath not giv'n His guid - ing o'er.
With His own great host He blends us, Lend - eth us of His own might.
As His own our bur - dens reck - on, As our own His strength pos - sess.

God is for us, God is for us; In His strength and stay we stand.
God is for us, God is for us; Help - ful now as here - to - fore.
God is for us, God is for us; Brings to hap - py end the fight.
God is for us, God is for us; God, our Help - er, still we bless.

God is for us, God is for us; In His strength and stay we stand.
God is for us, God is for us; Help - ful now as here - to - fore.
God is for us, God is for us; Brings to hap - py end the fight.
God is for us, God is for us; God, our Help - er, still we bless.

30 This is my Father's world

MALTBIE D. BABCOCK, Alt.

J. H. FILLMORE

1. This is my Father's World, And to my list-t'ning ears, All na-ture sings, and round me rings The mu-sic of the spheres. This is my Father's World, I rest me in the thot Of rocks and trees, of skies and seas, His hand the wonders wrought.

2. This is my Father's World, The birds their car-ols raise; The morn-ing light, the lil-y white, De-clare their Mak-er's praise. This is my Father's World, He shines in all that's fair; In the rus-tling grass I hear Him pass, He speaks to me ev-'ry-where.

3. This is my Father's World, O let me ne'er for-get That tho the wrong seems oft so strong, God is the Rul-er yet. This is my Father's World, The bat-tle now is won, But bound in love, thru God a-bove, Shall earth and heav'n be one.

31 There's a wideness in God's mercy

FREDERICK W. FABER, Alt. LIZZIE S. TOURJEE

1. There's a wide-ness in God's mer - cy, Like the wide-ness of the sea;
2. For the love of God is broad-er Than the meas-ure of man's mind;
3. Now our love is much more sim - ple, For we take Him at His word;

There's a kind-ness in His jus - tice, Which is more than lib - er - ty.
And the heart of the E - ter - nal Is most won - der - ful - ly kind.
And our lives are filled with sun-shine In the sweet-ness of our Lord.

32 Purer in heart, O God

MRS. A. L. DAVISON J. H. FILLMORE

1. Pur - er in heart, O God, Help me to be; May I de-
2. Pur - er in heart, O God, Help me to be; Teach me to
3. Pur - er in heart, O God, Help me to be; That I Thy

vote my life Whol - ly to Thee. Watch Thou my way - ward feet,
do Thy will Most lov - ing - ly. Be Thou my Friend and Guide,
ho - ly face Each day may see. Keep me from se - cret sin,

Purer in heart, O God

Guide me with coun - sel sweet; Pur - er in heart, Help me to be.
Let me with Thee a - bide; Pur - er in heart, Help me to be.
Reign Thou my soul with - in; Pur - er in heart, Help me to be.

33   Lord, for tomorrow and its needs

E. R. WILBERFORCE

H. R. PALMER

1. Lord, for to-mor-row and its needs I do not pray; Help me, my God, to
2. Let me both dil - i - gent-ly work, And du - ly pray; Let me be kind in
3. Let me be quick to do Thy will, Prompt to o - bey; Help me to con - se-

keep Thy law, Just for to - day. Let me be true in all I do,
word and deed, Just for to - day. Let me in sea - son, Lord, be grave,
crate my - self, Just for to - day. Lord, for to - mor - row and its needs

In all I say; Set Thou a seal up - on my lips, Just for to - day.
In sea - son gay; Let me be faith-ful to Thy grace, Just for to - day.
I do not pray; But keep me, guide me, love me, Lord, Just for to - day.

34
O what everlasting mercy

E. E. HEWITT

JNO. R. SWENEY

1. O, what ev - er - last - ing mer - cy Saved me, par - doned, and re-stored;
2. Make my life hence-forth a chan - nel, Where Thy love shall have its way;
3. Free, ex-haust - less is the foun - tain; Help me free - ly to be - lieve.

Fill me now to o - ver-flow - ing With Thy Ho - ly Spir - it, Lord.
Bless'd that I may be a bless - ing, Use me, Sav - iour, ev - 'ry day.
Riv - ers of Thy grace are prom - ised; More and more may I re - ceive.

Give me of the liv - ing wa - ter, Till my soul is sat - is - fied;
Clos - er, clos - er to the foun - tain, Hold my heart, my soul, my will:
Hap - py thirst that keeps me com - ing, Plead-ing still Thy gra - cious word;

From the wells of Thy sal - va - tion, Be my ev - 'ry need sup - plied.
Let the bless - ed heav'n-ly cur - rents, Rich - ly all my be - ing fill.
Fill me now to o - ver-flow - ing, With Thy Ho - ly Spir - it, Lord.

CHORUS

Fill me now, fill me now, To o - ver-flow - ing, to o - ver-
Fill me now, fill me now,

O what everlasting mercy

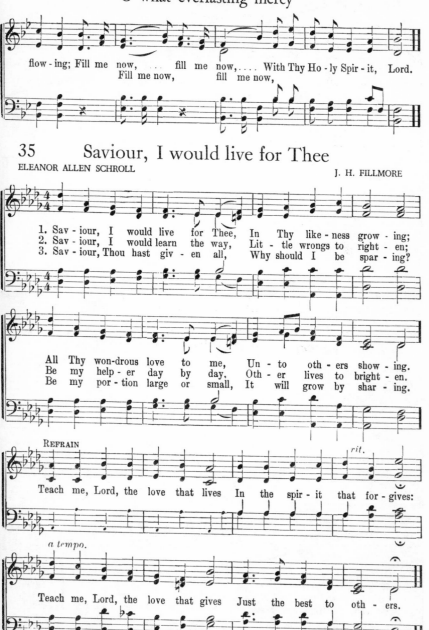

flow - ing; Fill me now, ... fill me now,.... With Thy Ho - ly Spir - it, Lord.
Fill me now, fill me now,

35   Saviour, I would live for Thee

ELEANOR ALLEN SCHROLL

J. H. FILLMORE

1. Sav - iour, I would live for Thee, In Thy like - ness grow - ing;
2. Sav - iour, I would learn the way, Lit - tle wrongs to right - en;
3. Sav - iour, Thou hast giv - en all, Why should I be spar - ing?

All Thy won-drous love to me, Un - to oth - ers show - ing.
Be my help - er day by day, Oth - er lives to bright - en.
Be my por - tion large or small, It will grow by shar - ing.

REFRAIN

rit.

Teach me, Lord, the love that lives In the spir - it that for - gives:

a tempo.

Teach me, Lord, the love that gives Just the best to oth - ers.

36 A Morning Prayer

(To Silent Unity.)

FAYETTE M. DRAKE.

ANNA LAURA DRAKE.

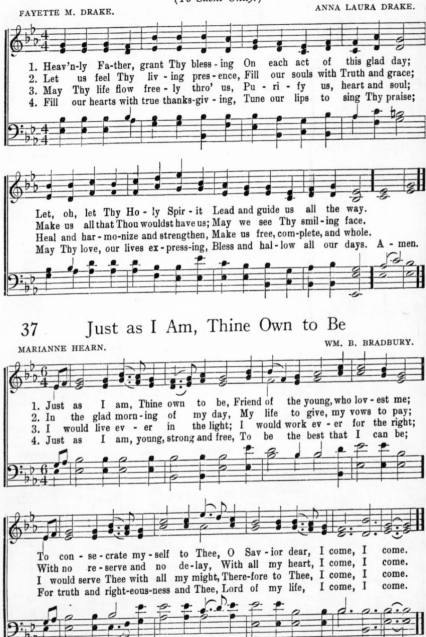

1. Heav'n-ly Fa-ther, grant Thy bless-ing On each act of this glad day;
2. Let us feel Thy liv-ing pres-ence, Fill our souls with Truth and grace;
3. May Thy life flow free-ly thro' us, Pu-ri-fy us, heart and soul;
4. Fill our hearts with true thanks-giv-ing, Tune our lips to sing Thy praise;

Let, oh, let Thy Ho-ly Spir-it Lead and guide us all the way.
Make us all that Thou wouldst have us; May we see Thy smil-ing face.
Heal and har-mo-nize and strengthen, Make us free, com-plete, and whole.
May Thy love, our lives ex-press-ing, Bless and hal-low all our days. A-men.

37 Just as I Am, Thine Own to Be

MARIANNE HEARN.

WM. B. BRADBURY.

1. Just as I am, Thine own to be, Friend of the young, who lov-est me;
2. In the glad morn-ing of my day, My life to give, my vows to pay;
3. I would live ev-er in the light; I would work ev-er for the right;
4. Just as I am, young, strong and free, To be the best that I can be;

To con-se-crate my-self to Thee, O Sav-ior dear, I come, I come.
With no re-serve and no de-lay, With all my heart, I come, I come.
I would serve Thee with all my might, There-fore to Thee, I come, I come.
For truth and right-eous-ness and Thee, Lord of my life, I come, I come.

Blest are the pure in heart

JOHN KEBLE.

J. H. FILLMORE.

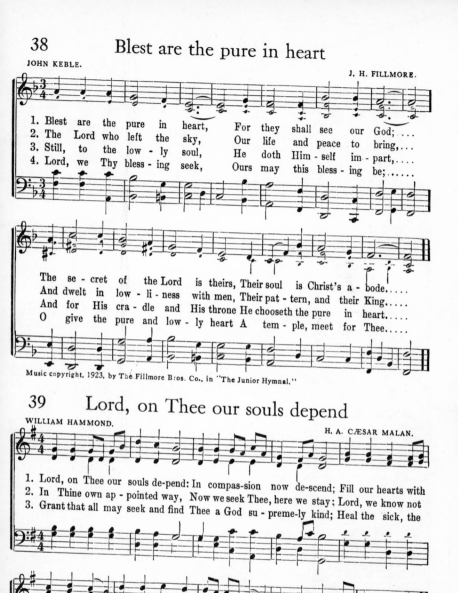

1. Blest are the pure in heart, For they shall see our God; ...
2. The Lord who left the sky, Our life and peace to bring,...
3. Still, to the low - ly soul, He doth Him - self im - part,....
4. Lord, we Thy bless - ing seek, Ours may this bless - ing be;......

The se - cret of the Lord is theirs, Their soul is Christ's a - bode.....
And dwelt in low - li - ness with men, Their pat - tern, and their King.....
And for His cra - dle and His throne He chooseth the pure in heart.....
O give the pure and low - ly heart A tem - ple, meet for Thee.....

Music copyright, 1923, by The Fillmore Bros. Co., in "The Junior Hymnal."

Lord, on Thee our souls depend

WILLIAM HAMMOND.

H. A. CÆSAR MALAN.

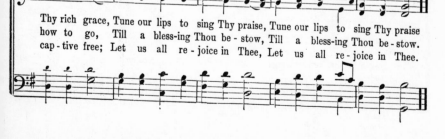

1. Lord, on Thee our souls de-pend: In compas-sion now de-scend; Fill our hearts with
2. In Thine own ap - pointed way, Now we seek Thee, here we stay; Lord, we know not
3. Grant that all may seek and find Thee a God su - preme-ly kind; Heal the sick, the

Thy rich grace, Tune our lips to sing Thy praise, Tune our lips to sing Thy praise,
how to go, Till a bless-ing Thou be - stow, Till a bless-ing Thou be - stow.
cap - tive free; Let us all re - joice in Thee, Let us all re - joice in Thee.

Bringing In the Sheaves

KNOWLES SHAW.

GEORGE A. MINOR.

1. Sow-ing in the morn-ing, sow-ing seeds of kind-ness, Sow-ing in the noon-tide
2. Sow-ing in the sun-shine, sow-ing in the shad-ows, Fear-ing nei-ther clouds nor

and the dew - y eve; Wait-ing for the har - vest, and the time of reap - ing,
win-ter's chill-ing breeze; By and by the har - vest, and the la - bor end - ed,

CHORUS

We shall come, re - joic - ing, bring-ing in the sheaves. Bring-ing in the sheaves,

bring - ing in the sheaves, We shall come, re - joic - ing, bring-ing in the sheaves,

Bringing in the sheaves, bringing in the sheaves, We shall come, rejoicing, bringing in the sheaves.

41 If I Would Serve

FRANCIS J. GABLE.

FRANGKISER.

1. If I would serve, if I would serve, I needs must know my fel-low-man, His part in
2. If I would serve, if I would serve, As God would have me serve His cause, I must for-
3. If I would serve, if I would serve, I must put tho'ts of self a-way; Just be con-
4. If I would serve, if I would serve, I may not flat-ter or con-demn; But ev-er

God's e-ter-nal plan; I must promote the best I can, If I would serve, if I would serve.
go the world's applause And strive to understand God's laws— If I would serve, if I would serve.
tent, from day to day, My problems at God's feet to lay, If I would serve, if I would serve.
"to the least of them" Bear Thruth's own gleaming di-a-dem, If I would serve, if I would serve.

42 I Can Hear My Savior Calling

EDWARD W. BLANDY.

ARR. FROM P. P. BLISS.

1. I can hear my Sav-ior call-ing, I can hear my Sav-ior call-ing,
2. I'll go with Him thro' the gar-den, I'll go with Him thro' the gar-den,
3. He will give me grace and glo-ry, He will give me grace and glo-ry,

CHO.—Where He leads me I will fol-low, Where He leads me I will fol-low,

ad lib. D. C. for Chorus.

I can hear my Sav-ior call-ing, "Take thy cross and fol-low, fol-low Me."
I'll go with Him thro' the gar-den, I'll go with Him, with Him all the way.
He will give me grace and glo-ry, And go with me, with me all the way.

Where He leads me I will fol-low, I'll go with Him, with Him all the way.

43 Saviour, teach me, day by day

JANE E. LEESON

C. M. VON WEBER

1. Sav - iour, teach me, day by day, Love's sweet les - son to o - bey;
2. With a child - like heart of love, At Thy bid - ding may I move;
3. Teach me all Thy steps to trace, Strong to fol - low in Thy grace;
4. Love in lov - ing finds em - ploy— In o - be - dience all her joy;

Sweet - er les - son can not be— Lov - ing Him who first loved me.
Prompt to serve and fol - low Thee— Lov - ing Him who first loved me.
Learn - ing how to love from Thee— Lov - ing Him who first loved me.
Ev - er new that joy will be— Lov - ing Him who first loved me.

44 Master, speak! Thy servant heareth

FRANCES R. HAVERGAL.

J. H. FILLMORE.

1. Mas - ter, speak! Thy serv - ant hear - eth, Long - ing for Thy gra - cious word,
2. Oft - en thru my heart is peal - ing Man - y an - oth - er voice than Thine;
3. Speak to me by name, O Mas - ter, Let me know it is to me;

Long - ing for Thy voice that cheer - eth; Mas - ter, let it now be heard.
Man - y an un - willed ech - o steal - ing From the walls of this Thy shrine.
Speak, that I may fol - low fas - ter, With a step more firm and free.

Master, speak! Thy servant heareth

I am list-'ning, Lord, for Thee; What hast Thou to say to me?
Let Thy longed-for ac-cents fall; Mas-ter, speak! and si-lence all.
Where the Shep-herd leads the flock, In the shad-ow of the rock.

45 Out of sadness into gladness

JESSIE BROWN POUNDS

J. H. FILLMORE

1. Out of sad-ness in-to glad-ness, Sav-iour, Thou hast bid-den me;
2. Out of ter-ror, out of er-ror, Out of all that dark-ness brings,
3. Out of seem-ing, out of dream-ing, Out of earth's un-cer-tain-ty,

In-to bless-ing, all pos-sess-ing, Out of self and in-to Thee.
In-to un-ion and com-mun-ion With the ho-ly King of kings.
In-to sure-ness and se-cure-ness—Out of self and in-to Thee.

REFRAIN.

Out of self and in-to Thee! Lord, Thy won-drous love I see;

Let me dai-ly far-ther flee, Out of self and in-to Thee.

New arrangement copyright, 1926, by The Fillmore Bros. Co., in "The New Praise Hymnal Revised."

46 We may not climb the heavenly steeps

JOHN GREENLEAF WHITTIER

Arr. from WILLIAM V. WALLACE

1. We may not climb the heav'n-ly steeps To bring the Lord Christ down;
2. But warm, sweet, ten-der, e-ven yet A pres-ent help is He;
3. The heal-ing of His seam-less dress Is by our beds of pain;
4. O Lord, and Mas-ter of us all, What-e'er our name or sign,

In vain we search the low-est deeps, For Him no depths can drown.
And faith has still its Ol-i-vet, And love its Gal-i-lee.
We touch Him in life's throng and press, And we are whole a-gain.
We own Thy sway, we hear Thy call, We test our lives by Thine.

47 Where cross the crowded ways

F. MASON NORTH

GERMANY

BEETHOVEN

1. Where cross the crowd-ed ways of life, Where sound the cries of race and clan,
2. In haunts of wretch-ed-ness and need, On shadowed thresholds dark with fears,
3. The cup of wa-ter giv'n for Thee, Still holds the fresh-ness of Thy grace;
4. Till sons of men shall learn Thy love And fol-low where Thy feet have trod:

A-bove the noise of self-ish strife, We hear Thy voice, O Son of man!
From paths where hide the lures of greed, We catch the vis-ion of Thy tears.
Yet long these mul-ti-tudes to see The sweet com-pas-sion of Thy face.
Till glo-rious from Thy heav'n a-bove Shall come the cit-y of our God.

48 My God, is any hour so sweet?

CHARLOTT ELLIOTT

J. H. FILLMORE

1. My God, is an-y hour so sweet, From blush of morn to even-ing star,
2. Blest is that tran-quil hour of morn, And blest that sol-emn hour of eve,
3. No words can tell what sweet re-lief There for my ev-'ry want I find;

As that which calls me to Thy feet, The hour of pray'r, The hour of pray'r?
When, on the wings of pray'r up-borne, The world I leave, The world I leave.
What strength for war-fare, balm for grief, What peace of mind! What peace of mind!

Music Copyright, 1920, by The Fillmore Bros. Co., in "Hymns for Today." International copyright.

49 The Prayer of Faith

HANNAH MORE KOHAUS

W. H. MONK

1. God is my help in ev-'ry need; God does my ev-'ry hun-ger feed,
2. I now am wise, I now am true, Pa-tient, kind, and lov-ing, too;
3. God is my health, I can't be sick; God is my strength, un-fail-ing, quick;

God walks beside me, guides my way Thru ev-'ry mo-ment of this day.
All things I am, can do, and be, Thru Christ the Truth, that is in me.
God is my all, I know no fear, Since God and love and Truth are here. A-men.

50   If I could but tell all the glory

ELEANOR ALLEN SCHROLL   J. H. FILLMORE

1. If I could but tell all the glo-ry That shines in my soul day by day;
2. If I could but tell of His goodness, His love, and His in-fi-nite care;
3. If I could but tell you of Je-sus, Of how I was saved by His grace;

Or if I could tell of the Sav-iour, Till ech-oes would ring it for aye;
Or if I could show you the vis-ion, I see when I meet Him in pray'r;
Or if I could paint the compassion I see in the dear Master's face;

I'd shout it a-loud from the mountain, I'd sing it o'er val-ley and plain;
Or if I could tell the old sto-ry Till oth-ers would feel He was near;
I'd sing till the far-a-way ech-oes, Would ring from the earth to the sky,

rit.

I'd tell it and tell it and tell it, Till mil-lions would hear the re-frain.
I'd tell it and tell it and tell it, All na-tions His prais-es would hear.
I'd tell it and tell it and tell it, In prais-es that nev-er would die.

REFRAIN.

But bet-ter than tell-ing is liv-ing A life ev-er faith-ful and true;
But bet-ter is liv-ing A life that is true;

If I could but tell all the glory

Then souls that are seeking to know Him, Will see .... Je-sus' love shining thru.
Then souls that would know Him, Will see Jesus' love shin - ing thru.

51 Open my eyes, that I may see

C. H. S.

CHAS. H. SCOTT

1. O - pen my eyes, that I may see Glimp-ses of truth Thou hast for me;
2. O - pen my ears, that I may hear Voic - es of truth Thou send - est clear;
3. O - pen my mouth, and let me bear Glad - ly the warm truth ev - 'ry where;

Place in my hands the won-der-ful key That shall un-clasp, and set me free.
And while the wave-notes fall on my ear, Ev - 'ry-thing false will dis - ap-pear.
O - pen my heart, and let me pre-pare Love with Thy chil - dren thus to share.

Si - lent - ly now I wait for Thee, Read-y, my God, Thy will to see;

O - pen my {eyes, ears, heart,} il - lum - ine me, Spir - it di - vine!

52 Send down Thy Truth, O God

EDWARD R. SILL

HORATIO W. PARKER

1. Send down Thy truth, O God; .... Too long the shad - ows frown,
2. Send down Thy spir - it free, ... Till wil - der - ness and town
3. Send down Thy love, Thy life, ... Our less - er lives to crown,
4. Send down Thy peace, O Lord, ... Earth's bit - ter voic - es drown

Too long the darkened way we've trod, Thy truth, O Lord, send down.
One tem - ple for Thy wor-ship be, Thy spir - it, O send down.
And cleanse them of their hate and strife, Thy liv - ing love send down.
In one deep o - cean of ac- cord, Thy peace, O God, send down. A - men.

53 All power is given unto me

THEODORE COMSTOCK

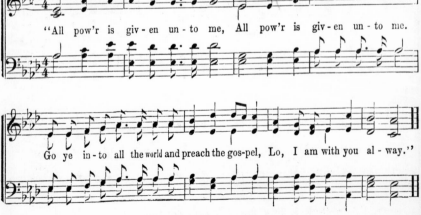

"All pow'r is giv - en un - to me, All pow'r is giv - en un - to me.

Go ye in - to all the world and preach the gos-pel, Lo, I am with you al - way."

54
Sweet hour of prayer

WILLIAM B. BRADBURY.

1. Sweet hour of pray'r, sweet hour of pray'r, In-fold-ed in the pres-ence rare
2. Sweet hour of pray'r, sweet hour of pray'r, In love with all men ev-'ry-where,
3. Sweet hour of pray'r, sweet hour of pray'r, In-to the "se-cret place" re-pair;

Of One who fills with Truth and Light, The One who works with wondrous might.
The u-ni-verse is but the whole Of all that is in man's pure soul.
I feel that quick'ning Life of Thine And know that Thine is al-so mine.

The still-ness of this si-lent hour Brings peace, good-will, and con-scious pow'r;
Thru Christ, the Truth, I now be-hold The broth-er-hood of man un-fold.
The light of Truth is now revealed; I sing with joy, for I am healed.

The time of si-lence is, to me, E-ter-nal joy and har-mo-ny.
Man thinks this lov-ing tho't and feels The beau-ty Christ, the Truth, re-veals.
The glo-ry of the Lord I've seen; At one with Him I'm kept se-rene.

The time of si-lence is, to me, E-ter-nal joy and har-mo-ny.
Man thinks this lov-ing tho't and feels The beau-ty Christ, the Truth, re-veals.
The glo-ry of the Lord I've seen; At one with Him I'm kept se-rene.

Irradiance

ERNEST C. WILSON.

FRANGKISER.

1. Oh, fill me with Thy pres-ence, Lord, That love may shine thro' me
2. Oh, fill me with Thy pres-ence, Lord, That wis-dom may be mine
3. Oh, fill me with Thy pres-ence, Lord, To guide what pow'r I wield,
4. Oh, fill me with Thy pres-ence, Lord, But need I lon-ger wait?

To quick-en that same pres-ence, Lord, In all whose eyes can see.
To share Thy light with all who need To let their own light shine.
That it may ev-er strength-en good And be from ill a shield.
Thy pres-ence hath been giv-en me To live and ra-di-ate!

56 Journey's End

ALFRED NOYES.

HERBERT J. WRIGHTSON.

Rather fast.

1. Know'st thou where that king-dom lies? Take no lan-thorn in thy hand,
2. Splen-dors of the sun grow dim, Stars are dark-ened by that light;
3. In that king-dom fold-ed lie All that eyes be-lieve they see;

Search not the un-fath-omed skies. Jour-ney not o'er sea and land,
Tho'ts that burn like ser-a-phim Throng thine in-ner world to-night.
All the hues of earth and sky, Time, space, and e-ter-ni-ty.

Abide with me

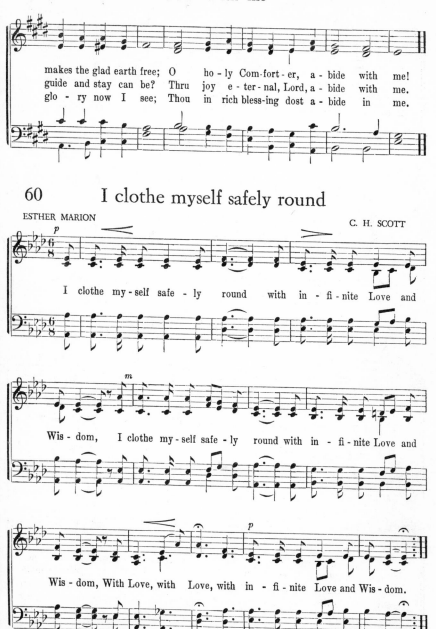

makes the glad earth free; O   ho - ly Com-fort - er, a - bide   with   me!
guide and stay can be? Thru   joy e - ter - nal, Lord, a - bide   with   me.
glo - ry now I see;   Thou   in rich bless-ing dost a - bide   in   me.

60   I clothe myself safely round

ESTHER MARION   C. H. SCOTT

I clothe my-self safe - ly   round   with in - fi - nite Love and

Wis - dom,   I clothe my-self safe - ly   round with in - fi - nite Love and

Wis - dom, With Love, with   Love, with in - fi - nite Love and Wis - dom.

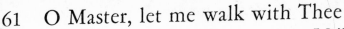

61 O Master, let me walk with Thee

WASHINGTON GLADDEN

T. R. MATTHEWS

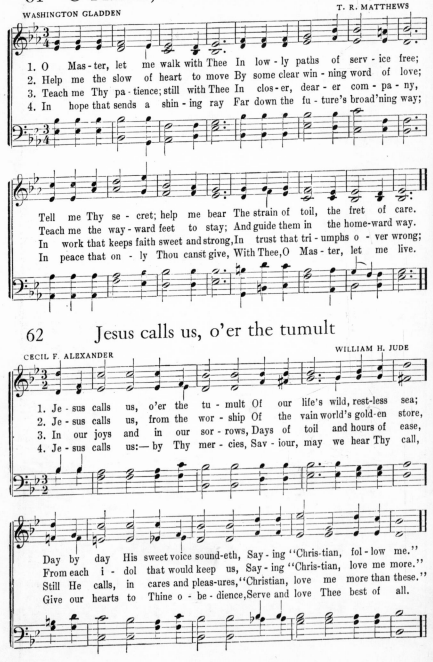

1. O Mas-ter, let me walk with Thee In low-ly paths of serv-ice free;
2. Help me the slow of heart to move By some clear win-ning word of love;
3. Teach me Thy pa-tience; still with Thee In clos-er, dear-er com-pa-ny,
4. In hope that sends a shin-ing ray Far down the fu-ture's broad'ning way;

Tell me Thy se-cret; help me bear The strain of toil, the fret of care.
Teach me the way-ward feet to stay; And guide them in the home-ward way.
In work that keeps faith sweet and strong, In trust that tri-umphs o-ver wrong;
In peace that on-ly Thou canst give, With Thee, O Mas-ter, let me live.

62 Jesus calls us, o'er the tumult

CECIL F. ALEXANDER

WILLIAM H. JUDE

1. Je-sus calls us, o'er the tu-mult Of our life's wild, rest-less sea;
2. Je-sus calls us, from the wor-ship Of the vain world's gold-en store,
3. In our joys and in our sor-rows, Days of toil and hours of ease,
4. Je-sus calls us:— by Thy mer-cies, Sav-iour, may we hear Thy call,

Day by day His sweet voice sound-eth, Say-ing "Chris-tian, fol-low me."
From each i-dol that would keep us, Say-ing "Chris-tian, love me more."
Still He calls, in cares and pleas-ures, "Christian, love me more than these."
Give our hearts to Thine o-be-dience, Serve and love Thee best of all.

63 There's a garden where Jesus is waiting

ELEANOR ALLEN SCHROLL

J. H. FILLMORE

1. There's a gar-den where Je-sus is wait-ing, There's a place that is
2. There's a gar-den where Je-sus is wait-ing, And I go with my
3. There's a gar-den where Je-sus is wait-ing, And He bids you to

won-drous-ly fair; For it glows with the light of His pres-ence, 'Tis the
bur-den and care; Just to learn from His lips words of com-fort, In the
come meet Him there; Just to walk and to talk with my Sav-iour, In the

REFRAIN

beau-ti-ful gar-den of prayer. O the beau-ti-ful gar-den, the

gar-den of prayer, O the beau-ti-ful gar-den of prayer; There my Sav-iour a-

waits, and He o-pens the gates, To the beau-ti-ful gar-den of prayer.

64   In the valley of silence

JESSIE BROWN POUNDS

J. H. FILLMORE

1. In the Val-ley of Si-lence I walk with my God, Where God and my
2. In the Val-ley of Si-lence I think of my sin, And long to be
3. In the Val-ley of Si-lence is nev-er a fear, For God will take

soul are a-lone; And o-ver the path that the an-gels have trod,
stain-less and pure; But God in His good-ness is speaking with-in,
care of His own; So firm-ly I walk, with-out tre-mor or tear,

REFRAIN

I press, with my hand in His own. (His own.) O Val-ley of Si-lence! O
To tell me His mer-cy is sure. (is sure.)
While God and my soul are a-lone. (a-lone.)

Val-ley of Rest, Where God and my soul are a-lone! (a-lone!) In the beau-ty and

still-ness I find sweet re-pose And peace, His sweet peace is my own. (my own.)

65 Be true to the best you know

JESSIE BROWN POUNDS

Risoluto.

1. Be true.... to the best you know; Be true to the dreams with-in;
2. Be true.... to your soul's best light; Be true to your life's best good;
3. Be true.... to the best you know, For hon-or is more than fame;

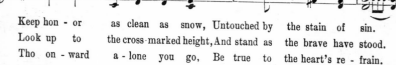

Keep hon - or as clean as snow, Untouched by the stain of sin.
Look up to the cross-marked height, And stand as the brave have stood.
Tho on - ward a - lone you go, Be true to the heart's re - frain.

REFRAIN.

Be true,.... be true, (be true,) He los - es who stoops to win! to win!

Be true, ... be true, (be true,) Be true to the dreams with - in! ...

66
Humility

FRANCIS J. GABLE.

FRANGKISER.

1. Know-ing my strength, I bend the knee To kneel be-side the weak;
2. Wis-dom is mine, yet all I know From Thee I hum-bly learn;
3. Know-ing the past, I ask Thee how The fu-ture must be run;

Know-ing my might, I yet beg Thee To give me what I seek.
Know-ing the way that I must go, I ask Thee where to turn.
Know-ing my pride, I meek-ly bow And say, "Thy will be done."

CHORUS.

Oh! hear-est Thou my plea...... I hum-bly ask of Thee,......

Not for a might-y pow-er, Lord, But more hu-mil-i-ty.

67
Nearer, My God, to Thee

SARAH F. ADAMS.

ARR. BY LOWELL MASON.

1. Near - er, my God, to Thee, Near - er to Thee! E'en though it
2. Though like the wan - der - er, The sun gone down, Dark - ness be
3. There let the way ap-pear, Steps un - to heav'n: All that Thou
4. Or if on joy - ful wing, Cleav - ing the sky, Sun, moon, and

Nearer, My God, to Thee

be   a   cross   That   rais - eth   me;   Still   all   my   song   shall   be,
o - ver   me,   My   rest   a   stone;   Yet   in   my   dreams   I'd   be,
send - est   me,   In   mer - cy   giv'n: An - gels   to   beck - on   me,
stars   for - got,   Up - wards   I'll   fly,   Still   all   my   song   shall   be,

Near - er, my God, to Thee, Near - er, my God, to Thee, Near - er to Thee!

68   Rock of Ages, Truth Divine

THOMAS HASTINGS.

1. Rock of a - ges, Truth di - vine, Strong foun - da - tion, ev - er mine;
2. On the rock of Truth I stand, Des - ti - ny at my com - mand;
3. For the ask - ing I at - tain Ev - 'ry height in Truth's do - main,

Safe, se - cure, I here re - main, In the peace He doth or - dain;
Filled with peace and pow'r of God, Bound-less good, e - ter - nal love;
Ev - 'ry wish with - in my heart; For no bless - ing can de - part.

Liv - ing ev - er in the light, Pure and per - fect in God's sight.
Safe with Truth, so firm and strong, Prais - ing in tri - um-phant song.
All of good is ev - er mine, On the rock of Truth di - vine. A - men.

69 Christ in the Soul

LAURA WOOD MARTIN.

FRANGKISER.

1. 'Tis sweet to know the still small voice That bids us trust, bids us re - joice And rec - og - nize the Son of God, The first be - got - ten of the Lord! His Spir - it reigns— the per - fect Son In all hu - man - i - ty as one! With love the Sav - ior does en - twine The broth - er - hood of Truth di - vine.

2. Like dark - ness when the light ap - pears Each ill dis - solves or dis - ap - pears, And we ex - press a glo - rious wealth Of ra - di - ant, tran - scend - ent health. For ev - 'ry pre - cious, ti - ny cell Re - sponds and tells us we are well. The pow - er of the in - ner Christ In - vig - or - ates with youth and life.

3. Re - deemed of God, stand forth to - day; There is no bet - ter time or way. Re - ceive the gra - cious Christ with - in, For He a - bides— the ris - en King! Life's rich - est gifts we may de - sire As in His name we do as - pire, And life a - bun - dant we com - mand Thro' Christ, when we but un - der - stand.

70   A Psalm of Praise

GRENVILLE KLEISER.

JOHN PROCTOR.

1. To Thee, O Lord, we ren - der thanks For all Thy mer - cies sure;
2. Teach us to know Thy per - fect will And tru - ly hum - ble be;
3. Thou art our ref - uge and our strength, There is no oth - er pow'r;
4. To Thee, O Lord, we ren - der thanks, And call up - on Thy name;

Thy ten - der love en - vi - rons us, And will thro' life en - dure.
May we in glad - ness praise Thy name Thro' all e - ter - ni - ty.
If sud - den dan - ger threat - ens us, We find in Thee a tow'r.
A psalm of praise to Thee we sing, Thy won - drous love pro - claim.

71   Dear Lord and Father of Mankind

JOHN G. WHITTIER.

FREDERICK C. MAKER.

1. Dear Lord and Fa - ther of man - kind, For - give our fe - v'rish ways; Re - clothe us in our
2. In sim - ple trust like theirs who heard, Be - side the Syr - ian sea, The gracious call - ing
3. Drop Thy still dews of qui - et - ness, Till all our striv - ings cease; Take from our souls the
4. Breathe thro' the heats of our de - sire Thy coolness and Thy balm; Let sense be dumb, let

right - ful mind; In pur - er lives Thy serv - ice find, In deep - er rev - 'rence praise.
of the Lord, Let us, like them, with - out a word, Rise up and fol - low Thee.
strain and stress, And let our or - dered lives con - fess The beau - ty of Thy peace.
flesh re - tire; Speak thro' the earth - quake, wind and fire, O still small voice of calm.

72 I Longed to See the Christ

F. B. WHITNEY.

FRANGKISER.

1. I longed to see the Christ, and lo, I saw the dawn-ing sun!
2. I longed to see the Christ; I saw a friend ex-tend a hand—
3. I longed to see the heal-ing Christ, and saw the sick a-rise;

It scat-tered mist and fog and gave its light to ev-'ry one.
The hand of Christ? Ah, yes, it sat-is-fied my heart's de-mand.
The voice of Truth ex-pressed had shorn dis-ease of its dis-guise.

I looked and saw the world that Christ had filled with beau-ty rare,
I saw a smile, but in that smile I saw a smile di-vine;
And then I learned the truth pro-found: If we of Christ would learn,

And as I looked I felt in-deed that Christ is ev-'ry-where.
The Christ had smiled up-on me thro' a friend, a friend of mine.
We must Him rec-og-nize in all and for Him we must yearn.

73
Just where thou art

E. A. H.

ELISHA A. HOFFMAN

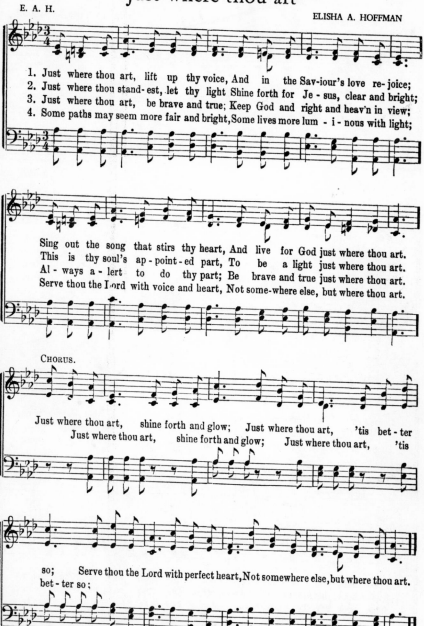

1. Just where thou art, lift up thy voice, And in the Sav-iour's love re-joice;
2. Just where thou stand-est, let thy light Shine forth for Je-sus, clear and bright;
3. Just where thou art, be brave and true; Keep God and right and heav'n in view;
4. Some paths may seem more fair and bright, Some lives more lum - i - nous with light;

Sing out the song that stirs thy heart, And live for God just where thou art.
This is thy soul's ap - point-ed part, To be a light just where thou art.
Al - ways a - lert to do thy part; Be brave and true just where thou art.
Serve thou the Lord with voice and heart, Not some-where else, but where thou art.

CHORUS.

Just where thou art, shine forth and glow; Just where thou art, 'tis bet - ter
Just where thou art, shine forth and glow; Just where thou art, 'tis

so; Serve thou the Lord with perfect heart, Not somewhere else, but where thou art.
bet - ter so;

74 The Morn of Truth Is Breaking

MARY E. BUTTERS.

ARR. BY LOWELL MASON.

1. The morn of Truth is break-ing; Ten thou-sand notes of love
2. Oh, reign in ev-'ry house-hold, And where there's one soul sad,
3. Come in, thou peace-ful an-gel, And ope the gates of day;

From tune-ful souls are wak-ing To swell the songs a-bove.
Come as a ra-diant an-gel— A light to make it glad.
With beams of liv-ing love-light, Chase all things false a-way.

Come, raise a glo-rious an-them Far o-ver hill and plain,
O Truth, shine on in splen-dor! Dis-pel these shades of gloom,
Thou art that light from heav-en To glow in ev-'ry soul;

For Truth in ra-diant splen-dor Has come on earth to reign.
And where there seems a des-ert, The rose shall burst in bloom.
Shine thou, O Truth! in splen-dor, As age on a-ges roll.

75
Sing a Little Song
(To My Coworkers.)

FRANGKISER.

1. Sing a lit-tle song, a lit-tle song of cheer, And bright-en up your heart to-day. Sing a lit-tle song, and sing it loud and clear, 'Twill chase a cloud of gloom a-way. Sing a song, sing a song, And you'll nev-er have a wor-ry all day long. It will thrill you, fill you with tho'ts of joy. Sing a song, sing a song, sing a song.

2. Sing a lit-tle song, a lit-tle song of love, And then your dreams will all come true. Sing a lit-tle song, and you'll be think-ing of The hap-pi-ness in store for you. Sing a song, sing a song; While you're sing-ing, you can right some lit-tle wrong. It will thrill you, fill you with tho'ts of love. Sing a song, sing a song, sing a song.

3. Sing a lit-tle song, a lit-tle song of praise, And ev-'ry one you meet will smile. Sing a lit-tle song, your joy-ous voic-es raise; Keep sing-ing, won't you, all the while. Sing a song, sing a song, For a mel-o-dy can guide you all day long. It will thrill you, fill you with tho'ts of life. Sing a song, sing a song, sing a song.

CHORUS

76 Love divine, all love excelling

JOHN ZUNDEL

1. Love di - vine, all love ex - cell - ing, Joy of heav'n, to earth come down!
2. Breathe, O breathe Thy lov - ing Spir - it In - to ev - 'ry faith - ful breast!

Fix in us Thy ho - ly dwell - ing, All Thy faith - ful mer - cies crown.
Let us all in Thee in - her - it, Let us find that per - fect rest.

Je - sus, Thou art all com - pas - sion, Pure, un - bound - ed love Thou art;
Fin - ish then Thy new cre - a - tion, Pure and spot - less let us be;

Vis - it us with Thy sal - va - tion, En - ter ev - 'ry trust - ing heart.
Show us now Thy great sal - va - tion Per - fect - ly re - stored thru Thee. A - men.

77 Praise to Thee, O Great Creator

1 Praise to Thee, O great Creator!
  Praise be Thine from every tongue;
O, let ev'ry living creature
  Join the universal song!
Spirit, Source of all our being,
  Free, eternal life is Thine;
Hail! the God of our salvation,
  Praise Him, He is Love Divine!

2 Riches come of Thee, and honor,
  Power and might to Thee belong;
Thine it is to make us prosper,
  Only Thine to make us strong.
Lord, to Thee, Thou God of mercy,
  Hymns of gratitude we raise;
To Thy name, forever glorious,
  Ever we address our praise!

78 O Zion, haste, thy mission high fulfilling

MARY ANN THOMSON and MYRTLE FILLMORE

JAMES WALCH

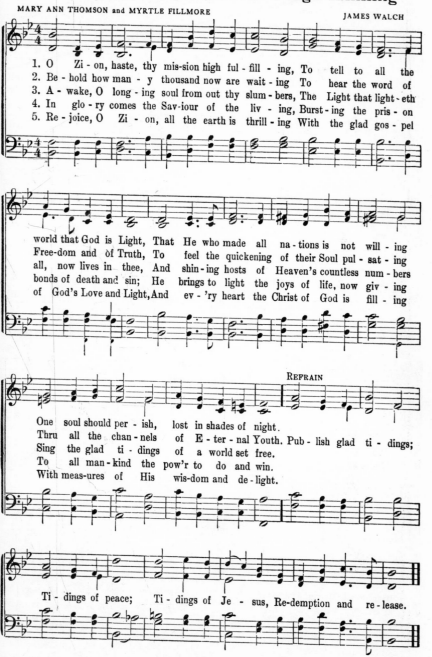

1. O Zi - on, haste, thy mis-sion high ful - fill - ing, To tell to all the
2. Be - hold how man - y thousand now are wait - ing To hear the word of
3. A - wake, O long - ing soul from out thy slum - bers, The Light that light - eth
4. In glo - ry comes the Sav-iour of the liv - ing, Burst-ing the pris - on
5. Re - joice, O Zi - on, all the earth is thrill - ing With the glad gos - pel

world that God is Light, That He who made all na - tions is not will - ing
Free-dom and of Truth, To feel the quickening of their Soul pul - sat - ing
all, now lives in thee, And shin-ing hosts of Heaven's countless num - bers
bonds of death and sin; He brings to light the joys of life, now giv - ing
of God's Love and Light, And ev - 'ry heart the Christ of God is fill - ing

REFRAIN

One soul should per - ish, lost in shades of night.
Thru all the chan - nels of E - ter - nal Youth. Pub - lish glad ti - dings;
Sing the glad ti - dings of a world set free.
To all man - kind the pow'r to do and win.
With meas-ures of His wis-dom and de - light.

Ti - dings of peace; Ti - dings of Je - sus, Re-demption and re - lease.

79 Come, let us join with faithful souls

WILLIAM G. LARRANT   HORATIO W. PARKER

1. Come, let us join with faith - ful souls Our song of faith to
2. And faith-ful are the gen - tle hearts To whom the power is
3. From step to step it wins its way A-gainst the hosts of

sing; .... One broth - er - hood in heart are we,
given,. .... Of ev - 'ry hearth to make a home,
sin; .... Part of the bat - tle - field is won,

And one our Lord and King. ..... Faith - ful are those who
Of ev - 'ry home a heaven...... O might - y host! no
And part is yet to win. .. Then join with faith - ful

love the truth, And dare the truth to tell; ..... Who stead - fast
tongue can tell The num - bers of its throng;.... No words can
heart and strong, And brave - ly on - ward go; ..... The tri - umphs

Come, let us join with faithful souls

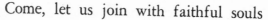

stand   at   God's   right   hand,   And   strive   to   serve   Him   well.
sound   the   mu - sic   vast   Of   its   grand   bat - tle   song.
that   a - wait   us   yet   Are   great - er   than   we   know.   A-men.

80   In Christ there is no East or West.

JOHN OXENHAM.   J. H. FILLMORE.

1. In   Christ   there   is   no   East   or   West,   In   Him   no   South   or   North;
2. Join   hands   then,   broth - ers   of   the   faith,   What-e'er   your   race   may   be,

But   one   great   fel - low - ship   of   Love   Thru - out   the   whole   wide   earth.
Who   serves   my   Fa - ther   as   a   son   Is   sure - ly   kin   to   me.

In   Him   shall   true   hearts   ev - 'ry-where   Their   high   com - mun - ion   find;
In   Christ   now   meet   both   East   and West,   In   Him   meet   South   and   North;

rit.

His   serv - ice   is   the   gold - en   cord   Close   bind - ing   all   man - kind.
All   Christ - ly   souls   are   one   in   Him   Thru - out   the   whole   wide   earth.

81   Hear the words of Wisdom calling

IONE G. DANIELS

LOWELL MASON

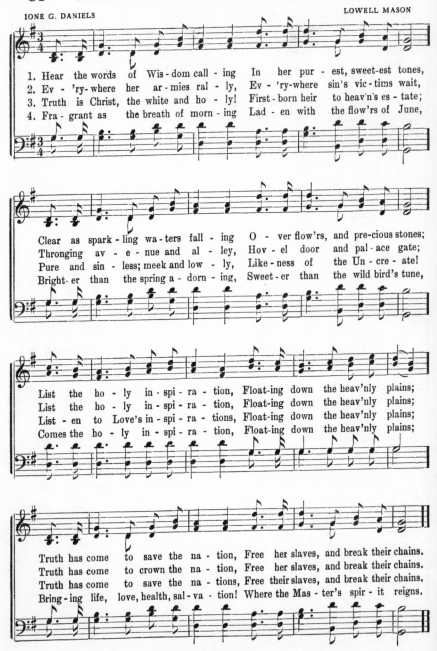

1. Hear the words of Wis-dom call-ing In her pur-est, sweet-est tones,
2. Ev-'ry-where her ar-mies ral-ly, Ev-'ry-where sin's vic-tims wait,
3. Truth is Christ, the white and ho-ly! First-born heir to heav'n's es-tate;
4. Fra-grant as the breath of morn-ing Lad-en with the flow'rs of June,

Clear as spark-ling wa-ters fall-ing O-ver flow'rs, and pre-cious stones;
Throng-ing av-e-nue and al-ley, Hov-el door and pal-ace gate;
Pure and sin-less; meek and low-ly, Like-ness of the Un-cre-ate!
Bright-er than the spring a-dorn-ing, Sweet-er than the wild bird's tune,

List the ho-ly in-spi-ra-tion, Float-ing down the heav'nly plains;
List the ho-ly in-spi-ra-tion, Float-ing down the heav'nly plains;
List-en to Love's in-spi-ra-tions, Float-ing down the heav'nly plains;
Comes the ho-ly in-spi-ra-tion, Float-ing down the heav'nly plains;

Truth has come to save the na-tion, Free her slaves, and break their chains.
Truth has come to crown the na-tion, Free her slaves, and break their chains.
Truth has come to save the na-tions, Free their slaves, and break their chains.
Bring-ing life, love, health, sal-va-tion! Where the Mas-ter's spir-it reigns.

82   Onward, comrades, Onward

HENRY VICTOR MORGAN

A. SULLIVAN

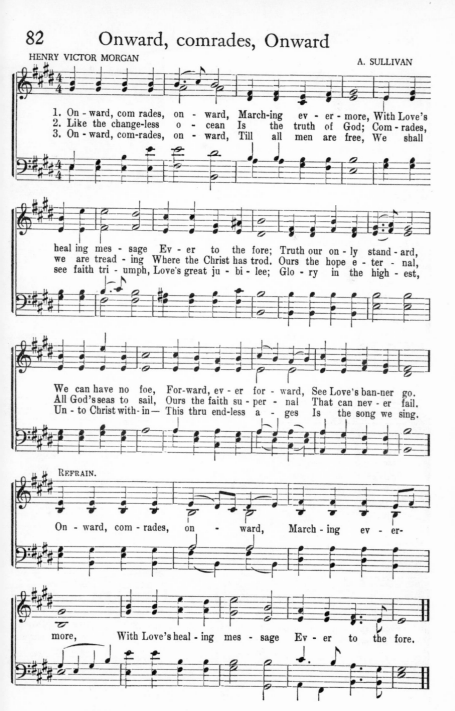

1. On - ward, com rades, on - ward, March-ing ev - er - more, With Love's
2. Like the change-less o - cean Is the truth of God; Com - rades,
3. On - ward, com-rades, on - ward, Till all men are free, We shall

heal ing mes - sage Ev - er to the fore; Truth our on - ly stand - ard,
we are tread - ing Where the Christ has trod. Ours the hope e - ter - nal,
see faith tri - umph, Love's great ju - bi - lee; Glo - ry in the high - est,

We can have no foe, For - ward, ev - er for - ward, See Love's ban-ner go.
All God's seas to sail, Ours the faith su - per - nal That can nev - er fail.
Un - to Christ with-in— This thru end-less a - ges Is the song we sing.

REFRAIN.

On - ward, com - rades, on - ward, March - ing ev - er-

more, With Love's heal - ing mes - sage Ev - er to the fore.

83   Wilt Thou Be Made Whole?

W. J. K.

WM. J. KIRKPATRICK

1. Hear the foot-steps of Je - sus, He is now pass-ing by, Bear-ing balm for the
2. 'Tis the voice of that Sav-iour, Whose mer- ci - ful call Free - ly of - fers sal-
3. Bless- ed Sav-iour, as - sist us To rest on Thy word; Let the soul-heal- ing

wound-ed, Healing all who ap - ply; As He spake to the suf - f'rer Who
va - tion To one and to all; He is now beck-'ning to Him Each
pow - er On us now be outpoured. Wash a - way ev - 'ry sin - spot, Take

lay at the pool, He is say - ing this moment: "Wilt thou be made whole?"
sin - taint - ed soul; And lov - ing - ly ask - ing: "Wilt thou be made whole?"
per - fect con - trol; Say to each trust - ing spir - it: "Thy faith makes thee whole."

CHORUS.

Wilt thou be made whole? Wilt thou be made whole? O come wea - ry

Wilt thou be made whole?

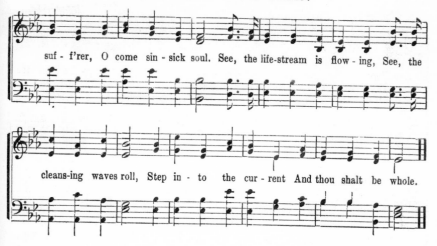

suf - f'rer, O come sin - sick soul. See, the life-stream is flow - ing, See, the
cleans-ing waves roll, Step in - to the cur - rent And thou shalt be whole.

84   Hear the footsteps of Jesus

1 Hear the footsteps of Jesus,
   He is now passing by,
Bearing balm and compassion,
   Healing all who apply;
As He spake to the loved one
   He found at the pool,
He is saying this moment;
   "O be thou made whole."

Chorus.

O be thou made whole,
   O be thou made whole;
Come into His presence,
   O come every soul.
See the life-stream is flowing,
   See, the cleansing waves roll,
Step into the current
   And thou art made whole.

2 'Tis the voice of the Saviour,
   Whose merciful call
Freely offers salvation
   To one and to all.

Lo! the Saviour stands waiting
   To strengthen your soul;
He is earnestly saying;
   "O be thou made whole."

3 Blessed Saviour, assist us
   To rest on Thy word;
May the soul-healing power
   On us now be outpoured.
Wash us white, cleanse and quicken
   Take perfect control;
Say to each trusting spirit;
   "Thy faith makes thee whole."

Chorus for last verse.

O I am made whole!
   O I am made whole!
I am quickened and strengthened,
   Mind, body, and soul.
Thru me now flows the life-stream,
   Free, its cleansing waves roll,
I enter the current
   And I am made whole!

85   Oh, Bliss of the Purified.

REV. FRANK BOTTOME. Alt.   WM. B. BRADBURY. Alt.

1. Oh, bliss of the pu - ri - fied, bliss of the free, I
2. Oh, bliss of the pu - ri - fied, Je - sus is mine, In
3. O Je - sus the glo - ri - fied! Thee will I sing, My

plunge in the heal - ing tide o - pened for me; The joy of re -
His bless - ed pres - ence and glo - ry I shine; In con - scious sal -
bless - ed Re-deem - er, my God and my King. My soul washed to

demp - tion ex - ult - ing I sing, Vic - to - rious for - ev - er, glad
va - tion I sing of His grace, Who lift - eth up - on me the
white - ness, His cleans - ing I feel, And tri - umph in life thro' the

CHORUS

prais - es I bring.
light of His face.   Oh, sing of His might - y love, Sing of His
"Might - y to heal."

rit.

might - y love, Sing of His might - y love, Might - y to heal.

86 God is love

C. H. S.

CLARA H. SCOTT

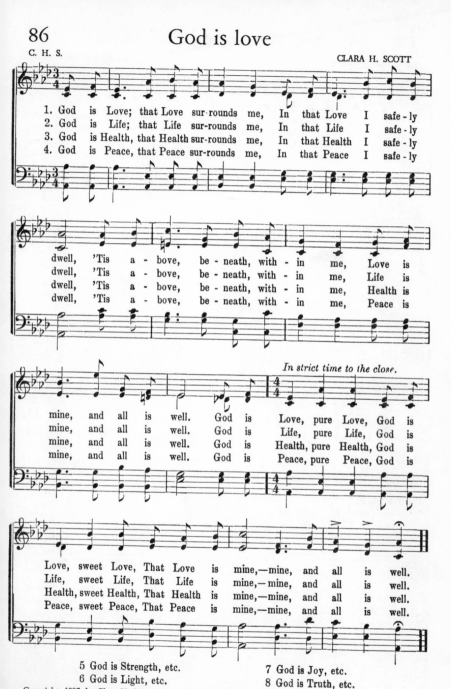

1. God is Love; that Love sur-rounds me, In that Love I safe-ly dwell, 'Tis a-bove, be-neath, with-in me, Love is mine, and all is well. God is Love, pure Love, God is Love, sweet Love, That Love is mine,—mine, and all is well.
2. God is Life; that Life sur-rounds me, In that Life I safe-ly dwell, 'Tis a-bove, be-neath, with-in me, Life is mine, and all is well. God is Life, pure Life, God is Life, sweet Life, That Life is mine,—mine, and all is well.
3. God is Health, that Health sur-rounds me, In that Health I safe-ly dwell, 'Tis a-bove, be-neath, with-in me, Health is mine, and all is well. God is Health, pure Health, God is Health, sweet Health, That Health is mine,—mine, and all is well.
4. God is Peace, that Peace sur-rounds me, In that Peace I safe-ly dwell, 'Tis a-bove, be-neath, with-in me, Peace is mine, and all is well. God is Peace, pure Peace, God is Peace, sweet Peace, That Peace is mine,—mine, and all is well.

In strict time to the close.

5 God is Strength, etc.
6 God is Light, etc.
7 God is Joy, etc.
8 God is Truth, etc.

87   We have heard the joyful sound

PRISCILLA J. OWENS   JESUS SAVES   WM. J. KIRKPATRICK

1. We have heard the joy - ful sound: Je - sus saves! Je - sus saves!
2. Waft it on the roll - ing tide; Je - sus saves! Je - sus saves!
3. Sing a - bove the bat - tle strife, Je - sus saves! Je - sus saves!
4. Give the winds a might - y voice: Je - sus saves! Je - sus saves!

Spread the tid - ings all a - round: Je - sus saves! Je - sus saves!
Tell to sin - ners far and wide: Je - sus saves! Je - sus saves!
By His death and end - less life, Je - sus saves! Je - sus saves!
Let the na - tions now re - joice,— Je - sus saves! Je - sus saves!

Bear the news to ev - 'ry land, Climb the steeps and cross the waves;
Sing, ye is - lands of the sea, Ech - o back, ye o - cean caves;
Sing it soft - ly thru the gloom, When the heart for mer - cy craves;
Shout sal - va - tion full and free, High - est hills and deep - est caves;

On - ward! 'tis our Lord's com-mand: Je - sus saves! Je - sus saves!
Earth shall keep her ju - bi - lee: Je - sus saves! Je - sus saves!
Sing in tri - umph o'er the tomb,— Je - sus saves! Je - sus saves!
This our song of vic - to - ry,— Je - sus saves! Je - sus saves!

88 We have heard the joyful sound

1 We have heard the joyful sound;
   Jesus heals! Jesus heals!
Spread the tidings all around;
   Jesus heals! Jesus heals!
Bear the news to every land
   Till the earth in homage kneels;
Onward! 'tis the Lord's command;
   Jesus heals! Jesus heals!

2 Waft it on the rolling tide;
   Jesus heals! Jesus heals!
Tell to nations far and wide;
   Jesus heals! Jesus heals!
Sing ye islands of the sea,
   Till mankind the glory feels,
Earth shall keep her jubilee;
   Jesus heals! Jesus heals!

3 Give the winds a mighty voice;
   Jesus heals! Jesus heals!
Let the nations now rejoice;
   Jesus heals! Jesus heals!
Shout the tidings full and free,
   Christ, His love to man reveals;
This our song of victory—
   Jesus heals! Jesus heals!

89 The Healer

J. G. WHITTIER   SCHUBERT

1. So stood of old the ho - ly Christ, A - midst the ea - ger throng,
2. That heal - ing gift is al - so theirs Who use it in His name;
3. For lo! in hu - man hearts un - seen, The Heal - er dwell - eth still,
4. That good Phy - si - cian liv - eth yet Thy friend and guide to be;

With whom His light - est touch suf - ficed To make His peo - ple strong.
The power that filled His gar-ment's hem Is ev - er-more the same.
And they who make His tem - ples clean, The best sub-serve His will.
The Heal - er by Gen-nes - ar - et Now lives and works thru thee. A - men.

90 I'm healed, praise God, I'm healed

PHILIP DODDRIDGE

LOWELL MASON

1. I'm healed, praise God, I'm healed, Thru Jesus Christ I'm healed;
2. Beneath His powerful sway His saints securely dwell;
3. His goodness stands approved, Unchanged from day to day;

Thru God, the everlasting Good, I'm healed, praise God, I'm healed.
That hand which bears all nature up Will guide His children well.
I'll drop my burden at His feet, And bear a song away.

4 I see, etc.
5 I hear, etc.
6 I'm rich, etc.

7 There's plenty for you and for me,
There's plenty for you and for me,
There's plenty for you, there's plenty for me.
There's plenty for you and for all.

91 He healeth me! O blessed thought

WM. B. BRADBURY

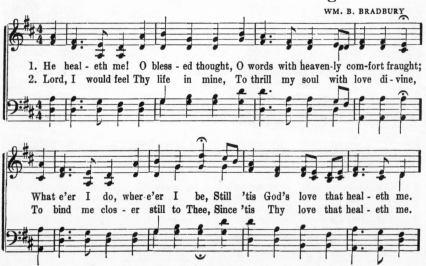

1. He healeth me! O blessed thought, O words with heaven-ly comfort fraught;
2. Lord, I would feel Thy life in mine, To thrill my soul with love divine,

What e'er I do, wher-e'er I be, Still 'tis God's love that healeth me.
To bind me closer still to Thee, Since 'tis Thy love that healeth me.

He healeth me! O blessed thought

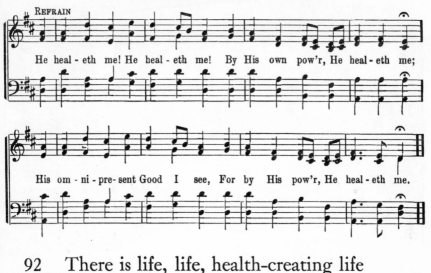

REFRAIN

He heal-eth me! He heal-eth me! By His own pow'r, He heal-eth me;

His om-ni-pre-sent Good I see, For by His pow'r, He heal-eth me.

92   There is life, life, health–creating life

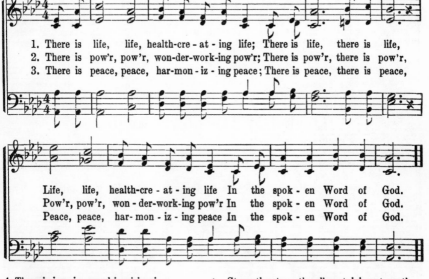

1. There is life, life, health-cre-at-ing life; There is life, there is life,
2. There is pow'r, pow'r, won-der-work-ing pow'r; There is pow'r, there is pow'r,
3. There is peace, peace, har-mon-iz-ing peace; There is peace, there is peace,

Life, life, health-cre-at-ing life In the spok-en Word of God.
Pow'r, pow'r, won-der-work-ing pow'r In the spok-en Word of God.
Peace, peace, har-mon-iz-ing peace In the spok-en Word of God.

4 There is joy, joy, soul-inspiring joy;
    There is joy, there is joy,
Joy, joy, soul-inspiring joy
    In the spoken Word of God.

2 There is strength, strength, all-sustaining
    strength,
There is strength, there is strength,

Strength, strength, all-sustaining strength
    In the spoken Word of God.

6 There is love, love, never-failing love;
    There is love, there is love,
Love, love, never-failing love,
    In the spoken Word of God.

93   Jesus is ever near

ELEANOR ALLEN SCHROLL   ARTHUR S. SULLIVAN

1. Je - sus is ev - er near, Guid - ing the way, Read - y to
2. Je - sus is ev - er near, Love to be - stow; Noth - ing have
3. Je - sus is ev - er near, Sing we His praise; May we His

help and cheer, All thru the day. Then when the shad - ows creep,
we to fear Wher - e'er we go. Striv - ing to do our best,
name re - vere Thru all our days. May we to oth - ers show

He will a vig - il keep, When-e'er His chil-dren sleep Je - sus is near.
We shall be tru - ly blest, Know-ing, thru ev - 'ry test, Je - sus is near.
His ten - der love, a - glow, Till ev - 'ry heart may know Je - sus is near.

Words copyright, 1923, by The Fillmore Bros. Co., in "The Junior Hymnal."

94   Healed by His power divine

Healed, healed by His pow'r di - vine! One, one with His love sub-lime! My

life now is sweet and my joy is com-plete, For I'm healed, healed, healed!
I'm healed!

95 I will sing you a song

ELLEN H. GATES. Alt.

PHILIP PHILLIPS

1. I will sing you a song Of a beau - ti - ful land—
2. I shall sing of the earth And the world when re - deemed,
3. In that mar - vel - ous land, Where the Riv - er of Life

In the Bi - ble the sto - ry is told—Where no cares ev - er
When re - stored as the gar - den of God, Where the Prince of all
Clear as crys - tal and pure ev - er flows, There the fruit la - den

come, Nev - er dark - ness nor gloom, And noth - ing shall ev - er grow
peace In His love reigns su - preme, And noth - ing shall ev - er grow
trees Ev - er bloom, ev - er bear, And noth - ing can ev - er grow

old, And noth - ing shall ev - er grow old; Where no cares ev - er
old, And noth - ing shall ev - er grow old; Where the Prince of all
old, And noth - ing can ev - er grow old; There the fruit la - den

come, Nev - er dark-ness nor gloom, And noth - ing shall ev - er grow old.
peace, In His love reigns su-preme, And noth - ing shall ev - er grow old.
trees Ev - er bloom, ev - er bear, And noth - ing can ev - er grow old.

Knowing

IRENE STANLEY

LOUISE BRIGHAM

1. God is my health, I am know-ing it now, My pow-er, my
2. God is my wealth, I am know-ing it now, No seem-ing pri-
3. God is my help, I am know-ing it now, My in-stant pro-

life, and my strength the day long. To sick-ness or sor-row I
va-tion my spir-it shall daunt, For I know that my Fa-ther will
tec-tion when dan-ger comes near. I am safe with the crown of His

nev-er need bow; I am filled with His joy, and e-ter-nal-ly
nev-er al-low A child of His king-dom to suf-fer from
love on my brow; All the earth is His realm, there is noth-ing to

strong. I am clear-ly and con-scious-ly know-ing it now.
want. I am clear-ly and con-scious-ly know-ing it now.
fear. I am clear-ly and con-scious-ly know-ing it now.

97 Jesus, Savior, Pilot Me

EDWARD HOPPER

JOHN E. GOULD

1. Je - sus, Sav - ior, pi - lot me   O - ver life's tem-pes-tuous sea;
2. As a moth - er stills her child,   Thou canst hush the o - cean wild;
3. I re - joice, for I am healed   By the pow'r Thou hast re - vealed;

Un-known waves be - fore me roll,   Hid - ing rock and treach'rous shoal;
Bois-t'rous waves o - bey Thy will   When Thou say'st to them, "Be still!"
Now I live, un-bound-ed, free,   In the love Thou hast for me;

Chart and com - pass come from Thee,   Je - sus, Sav - ior, pi - lot me.
Won-drous sov - 'reign of the sea,   Je - sus, Sav - ior, pi - lot me.
Life e - ter - nal now is mine   By Thy grace of love di - vine.

98 Father, Lead Me Day by Day

JOHN P. HOPPS

J. H. FILLMORE

1. Fa - ther, lead me day by day,   In Thine own, Thy per - fect way;
2. When in dan - ger make me brave,   Trust - ing in Thy pow'r to save;
3. When I'm tempt - ed to do wrong,   Make me stead - fast, wise, and strong;

Teach me to be pure and true,   Show me what I ought to do.
Keep me safe - ly by Thy side;   Let me in Thy love a - bide.
And when all a - lone I stand,   Shield me with Thy might - y hand.

99 Life, Love, Truth

GERALDINE D. ROBINSON

PLUMA M. BROWN

1. In the life of Om-ni-pres-ence Do I dwell,
2. In the love of Om-ni-pres-ence Do I rest,
3. In the Truth of Om-ni-pres-ence Do I stand,
4. Life and love and Truth, for-ev-er Thou art mine!

'Tis a-bove, a-round, with-in me, All is well;
Feel it fill-ing, thrill-ing thro' me, Bless-ed guest!
For the pow'r of the Al-might-y Holds my hand.
Glo-rious trin-i-ty of heav-en, All-di-vine.

Life di-vine for-ev-er guid-ing All my ways,
Love di-vine all dis-cord sooth-ing In-to peace,
Truth di-vine, su-preme, un-chang-ing, All art thou!
Oh, my soul doth sing with rap-ture Hymns of praise,

Life di-vine for-ev-er fill-ing All my days.
Love di-vine in whose sweet pres-ence Pain doth cease.
Truth di-vine, thy word is free-dom, Spo-ken now.
And my feet shall walk with glad-ness In thy ways.

100 Our Prayer

F. B. WHITNEY

HERBERT J. WRIGHTSON

1. I am one with God, my Fa - ther; In the heav'n-ly place we dwell.
2. As our thought in heav'n-ly plac - es, So on earth our will is done.
3. We thro' love for - give our debt - ors, All who tres - pass we for - give.
4. I am one with God, my Fa - ther. To me life and love He gives;

Hal - lowed is our sanc - tu - a - ry; I'm with God and all is well.
From our love we give so free - ly Dai - ly bread to ev - 'ry one.
From dis - ease and death we res - cue, And we teach to love and live.
U - ni - fied with me, e - ter - nal In my mind and heart He lives.

101 Prince of Peace, Control My Will

MARY A. S. BARBER

W. T. PORTER

1. Prince of Peace, con - trol my will; Bid this strug-gling heart be still;
2. May Thy will, not mine, be done; May Thy will and mine be one.
3. Sav - ior, at Thy feet I fall, Thou my life, my God, my all;

Bid my fears and doubt - ings cease; Hush my spir - it in - to peace.
Chase these doubt-ings from my heart, Now Thy per - fect peace im - part.
Let Thy hap - py serv - ant be One for - ev - er - more with Thee.

102 Go not abroad in search of Him

HENRY W. GREATOREX

1. Go not a-broad in search of Him, To no far land re - pair,
2. O Gift of gifts! O Grace of grace! That om - ni - pres - ent Good
3. So wan - der not in search of Him But to thy - self re - pair,

Nor to the depths of cav-erns dim, Nor heights of up - per air.
Makes of our hearts His dwell-ing-place, In lov - ing Fa - ther-hood.
Where si - lent rev-'rence reigns with-in, And thou shalt find Him there. A - men.

103 Lead us, O Father, in the paths.

WILLIAM H. BURLEIGH

JOSEPH BARNBY

1. Lead us, O Fa - ther, in the paths of peace; With - out Thy
2. Lead us, O Fa - ther, in the paths of truth; Un - helped by
3. Lead us, O Fa - ther, in the paths of right; Blind - ly we
4. Lead us, O Fa - ther, to Thy heaven - ly rest, How - ev - er

guid - ing hand we go a - stray, And doubts ap - pall, and
Thee, in er - 1or's maze we grope, While pas - sion stains and
stum - ble when we walk a - lone, In - volved in shad - ows
rough and steep the path - way be, Thru joy or sor - row,

Lead us, O Father, in the paths

sor-rows still in-crease; Lead us, thru Christ, the true and liv - ing Way.
fol - ly dims our youth, And age comes on uncheered by faith or hope.
of a mor - al night; On - ly with Thee we jour-ney safe - ly on.
as Thou deemest best, Un - til our lives are per - fect - ed in Thee. A-men.

104   Holy Spirit, Source of gladness

Tr. fr. P. GERHARDT

MOZART

1. Ho - ly Spir - it, Source of glad-ness! Come with all Thy ra - diance bright;
2. Let the peace which knows no meas-ure, Now in quick'ning show'rs de - scend,

O'er our sense of toil and sad - ness Breathe Thy life, and shed Thy light;
Bring-ing us the rich - est treas-ure Man can wish or God can send:

Send us Thine il - lu - mi - na - tion; Ban - ish all our soul's an - noy;
Hear our earn - est sup - pli - ca - tion, Ev - 'ry strug-gling heart re - lease;

Rest up - on this con - gre - ga - tion, Spir - it of un - fail - ing joy!
Rest up - on this con - gre - ga - tion, Spir - it of un - troub - led peace!

105 O love divine! where'er I am

HANNAH MORE KOHAUS

German Melody

1. O Love di-vine! wher-e'er I am, Thou dost a-bide with me;
2. O Love di-vine! what-e'er be-fall, If good or ill my lot;
3. Se-cure-ly may I trust in Thee, Thou love di-vine so sure;

What-ev-er path in life I take, I still re-main in Thee;
What-ev-er I may bring to pass, O Love! Thou chang-est not;
Un-moved as the e-ter-nal hills, Thou dost for aye en-dure;

For Thou art here and ev-'ry-where, Thou fill-est ev-'ry spot;
Thou art the same un-va-ry-ing, Thru-out e-ter-ni-ty;
O Love di-vine! I would be filled With sub-stance like to Thee,

O ev-er-pres-ent Love di-vine, O Love! Thou mov-est not.
All-stead-fast, change-less, help-ful, good, O Love! art Thou to me.
That Thou and I for-ev-er-more May in-ter-wo-ven be.

106 O life, that maketh all things new

WILLIAM B. BARDBURY

1. O Life, that mak-eth all things new, The bloom-ing earth, the
2. From hand to hand the greet-ing flows; From eye to eye the
3. One in the free-dom of the Truth; One in the joy of
4. The fre-er step, the full-er love, The wide ho-ri-zon's

tho'ts of men! Our pil-grim feet, wet with thy dew, In
sig-nals run; From heart to heart the bright faith glows; The
paths un-trod; One in the soul's per-en-nial youth; One
grand-er view, The peace that com-eth from a-bove, The

CHORUS

glad-ness hith-er turn a-gain.
seek-ers of the Light are one. U-nit-ed in the Truth we stand,
in the larg-er tho't of God.
life that mak-eth all things new.

Pro-claim-ing peace to ev-'ry land, Pro-claim-ing peace to ev-'ry land.

107 I am stronger than my fears

HANNAH MORE KOHAUS

A. S. SULLIVAN

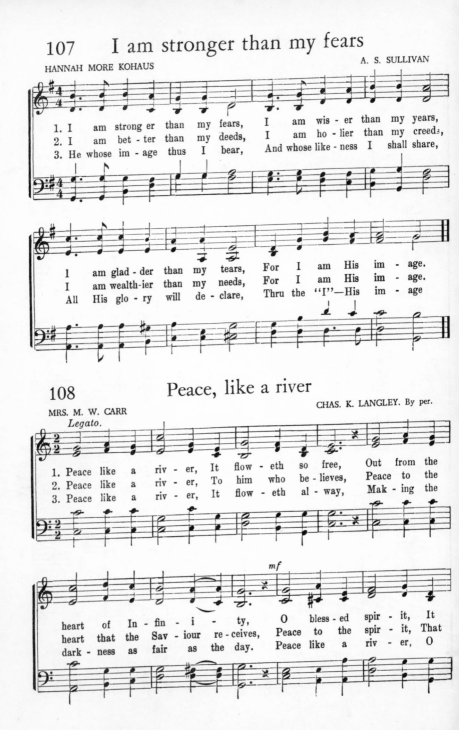

1. I am strong er than my fears, I am wis - er than my years,
2. I am bet - ter than my deeds, I am ho - lier than my creeds,
3. He whose im - age thus I bear, And whose like - ness I shall share,

I am glad - der than my tears, For I am His im - age.
I am wealth-ier than my needs, For I am His im - age.
All His glo - ry will de - clare, Thru the "I"—His im - age

108 Peace, like a river

MRS. M. W. CARR

CHAS. K. LANGLEY. By per.

Legato.

1. Peace like a riv - er, It flow - eth so free, Out from the
2. Peace like a riv - er, To him who be - lieves, Peace to the
3. Peace like a riv - er, It flow - eth al - way, Mak - ing the

mf

heart of In - fin - i - ty, O bless - ed spir - it, It
heart that the Sav - iour re - ceives, Peace to the spir - it, That
dark - ness as fair as the day. Peace like a riv - er, O

Peace, like a River

flow - eth for thee, Peace like a riv - er, Peace like a riv - er.
sor - rows and grieves, Peace like a riv - er, Peace like a riv - er.
wea - ry one, pray For Peace like a riv - er, Peace like a riv - er.

109   Jesus keeps me, O how precious.

ELEANOR ALLEN SCHROLL

J. H. FILLMORE

1. Je - sus keeps me, O how pre - cious! Sweet com-mun-ion here have we;
2. Grace and mer - cy nev - er ceas - ing, He is shed-ding on my way;
3. I am His, O blest as - sur - ance! Burst my soul with rap ture sweet;

O the per - fect peace of dwell - ing, I in Him, and He in me.
He has made my heart His tem - ple, Life is rich - er day by day.
He is mine, O won drous sto - ry! Love a - maz - ing, joy com-plete!

CHORUS.

Je - sus in my heart a - bid - ing, O the taste of joy di - vine;

On His bos-om safe - ly hid - ing, I am His and He is mine.

The Chant of the Ongoers

F. B. WHITNEY

FRANGKISER

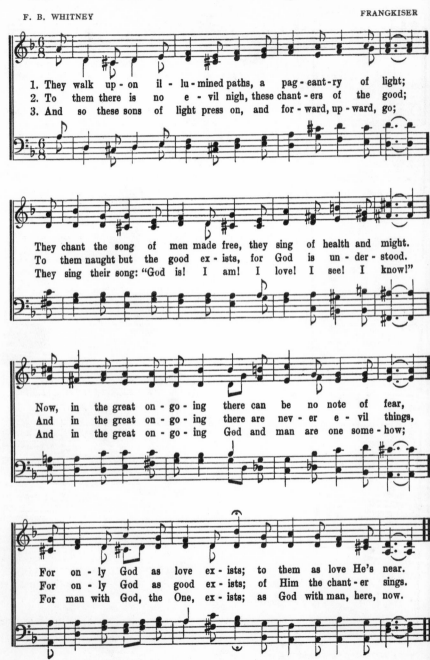

1. They walk up-on il-lu-mined paths, a pag-eant-ry of light;
2. To them there is no e-vil nigh, these chant-ers of the good;
3. And so these sons of light press on, and for-ward, up-ward, go;

They chant the song of men made free, they sing of health and might.
To them naught but the good ex-ists, for God is un-der-stood.
They sing their song: "God is! I am! I love! I see! I know!"

Now, in the great on-go-ing there can be no note of fear,
And in the great on-go-ing there are nev-er e-vil things,
And in the great on-go-ing God and man are one some-how;

For on-ly God as love ex-ists; to them as love He's near.
For on-ly God as good ex-ists; of Him the chant-er sings.
For man with God, the One, ex-ists; as God with man, here, now.

111 What a fellowship, what a joy divine.

REV. E. A. HOFFMAN   A. J. SHOWALTER

1. What a fel-low-ship, what a joy di-vine, Lean-ing on the ev-er-
2. O how sweet to walk in this pil-grim way, Lean-ing on the ev-er-
3. What have I to dread, what have I to fear, Lean-ing on the ev-er-

last-ing arms; What a bless-ed-ness, what a peace is mine,
last-ing arms; O how bright the path grows from day to day,
last-ing arms; I have bless-ed peace with my Lord so near,

REFRAIN.

Lean-ing on the ev-er-last-ing arms. Lean - ing,
Lean-ing on Je-sus,

lean - - ing   Safe and se-cure from all a-larms;
Lean - ing on Je - sus,

Lean - ing, lean - ing, Lean-ing on the ev-er-last-ing arms.
Lean-ing on Je-sus, lean-ing on Je-sus,

By permission of A. J. Showalter.

112 God Always Helps

EVELYN WHITELL   MILTON SPRENG

1. These words I in-ward-ly re-peat When tri-als seem too hard to
2. And when my path I can-not see, And noth-ing is re-vealed to
3. I   speak these words mid noise and strife, When in the rush of cit-y

meet; When thoughts of doubt rise in the way, I look them
me, I know I do not need to fear; I stand and
life; They lift from me the weight of care Like prom-ised

Chorus

in the face and say: God al-ways helps, our way He guides,
wait for mists to clear.
an-swer to a prayer.

And His dear love each day pro-vides; His bless-ings round a-bout us

flow. O world, lift up your head, and know God al-ways helps.

The Joy of Living

JONATHAN HUGHES ARNETT   JONATHAN HUGHES ARNETT

1. I am the joy, the joy of liv-ing; It comes from giv-ing,
2. I am the joy, the joy of liv-ing; It comes from giv-ing,
3. I am the joy, the joy of liv-ing; It comes from giv-ing,

giv - ing, giv - ing. I give of love, I give of peace, I
giv - ing, giv - ing. I give of strength, I give of pow'r, I
giv - ing, giv - ing. I give of hope, I give of cheer, I

nev - er cease.......
ev - 'ry hour.......
with - out a tear.......

give of joys that nev - er, nev - er cease. I am the joy, the
give of joys for ev - 'ry, ev - 'ry hour. I am the joy, the
give of joys with - out, with-out a tear. I am the joy, the

joy of liv - ing; It comes from giv - ing, giv - ing, giv - ing.
joy of liv - ing; It comes from giv - ing, giv - ing, giv - ing.
joy of liv - ing; It comes from giv - ing, giv - ing, giv - ing.

114   My Shepherd is the Lord

1. My Shep-herd is the Lord, my God, There is no want I know;
2. He doth re-store my faint-ing soul, With His di-vine ca-ress,
3. Yea, tho I walk the vale of death, What e-vil shall I fear?
4. Good-ness and mer-cy shall be mine Un-to my chang-ing day;

His flock He leads in ver-dant meads, Where tran-quil wa-ters flow.
And, when I stray, He points the way To paths of right-eous-ness.
Thy staff and rod are mine, O God, And Thou, my Shep-herd near!
There will I bide at His dear side For-ev-er and for aye.

115   God will take care of you

C. D. MARTIN   W. S. MARTIN

1. Be not dis-mayed, what-e'er be-tide, God will take care of you;
2. Thru days of toil when heart doth fail, God will take care of you;
3. All I may need He will pro-vide, He will take care of me;
4. No mat-ter what may be the test, God will take care of us;

Be-neath His wings of love a-bide; God will take care of you.
When dan-gers fierce your path as-sail, God will take care of you.
Noth-ing I ask will be de-nied; God will take care of me.
Lean, trust-ing one, up-on His breast; God will take care of us.

God will take care of you

CHORUS

God will take care of you, Thru ev-'ry day, O'er all the way;

He will take care of you, God will take care of you......
take care of you.

116 Our Father in Heaven

LUCIA MAY SMITH

1. Our Fa-ther in heav-en, we hal-low Thy name, May Thy king-dom
2. For-give our trans-gres-sions, and teach us to know, The hum-ble com-

ho-ly on earth be the same O give to us dai-ly our
pas-sion that par-dons each foe; Keep us from temp-ta-tion, from

por-tion of bread, It is from Thy boun-ty that all must be fed.
weakness and sin, And Thine be the glo-ry for-ev-er, A-men. A-men.

Music copyright, 1918, by Lucia May Smith.

117 **Immortal Love, forever full**

J. G. WHITTIER

Arr. from HAYDN

1. Im - mor - tal Love, for - ev - er full, For - ev - er flow - ing free,
2. Our out - ward lips con - fess the name All oth - er names a - bove;
3. Hush ev - 'ry lip, close ev - 'ry book, The strife of tongues for - bear;
4. O Love! O Life! our faith and sight Thy pres - ence mak - eth one:
5. The let - ter fails, the sys - tems fall, And ev - 'ry sym - bol wanes;

For - ev - er shared, for - ev - er whole, A nev - er - ebb - ing sea.
Love on - ly know - eth whence it came, And com - pre - hend - eth love.
Why for - ward reach, or back - ward look, For love that clasps like air?
As thru trans - fig - ured clouds of white We trace the noon - day sun.
The Spir - it o - ver - brood - ing all, E - ter - nal Love, re - mains.

118 **Our Father never faileth.**

G. J. WEBB.

1. Our Fa - ther nev - er fail - eth To give His chil - dren bread; They on - ly need to
2. Our Fa - ther nev - er fail - eth To give His off - spring strength; They need but lean, to
3. Our Fa - ther, God, the On - ly, Is 'round and in us all, Sus - tain - ing and em-

hun - ger, More rich - ly to be fed; For Love's abund - ant ta - ble Most gra - cious-
meas-ure Its height and breadth and length. "Lo! I am with you al ways!" This is the
brac - ing, That none need ev - er fall. He's light and joy and heal-ing, O come and

Our Father never faileth

ly sup-plies Each earn-est as-pi-ra-tion, That hour-ly doth a-rise.
prom-ise true, That knows no shade nor turn-ing, Be-lov-ed, meant for you.
taste and see; Our Fa-ther fail-eth nev-er Thru-out e-ter-ni-ty.

119   Father eternal

HANNAH MORE KOHAUS

J. CRAMER

1. Fa - ther e - ter - nal!—Life pure and un - de - filed, Food for the
2. Fa - ther su - per - nal!—Thou nev - er - fail - ing Love, Com - ing from
3. Fa - ther Al - might - y!—Swift - ly our souls a - rise, To that which

rec - on - ciled, O liv - ing bread! Bread with all sub-stance rife,
realms a - bove O liv - ing bread! Bread with all whole-ness fraught,
sat - is - fies, O liv - ing bread! Ra - diant its light shall be,

Heal - ing all pain and strife, Breath of e - ter - nal Life, O liv - ing bread!
Fra - grant with ho - ly tho't, On an - gels' pin-ions bro't, O liv - ing bread!
Shin - ing e - ter - nal - ly, With us in u - ni - ty, O liv - ing bread!

120 Lo! the army of our King

A. P. COBB

J. H. FILLMORE

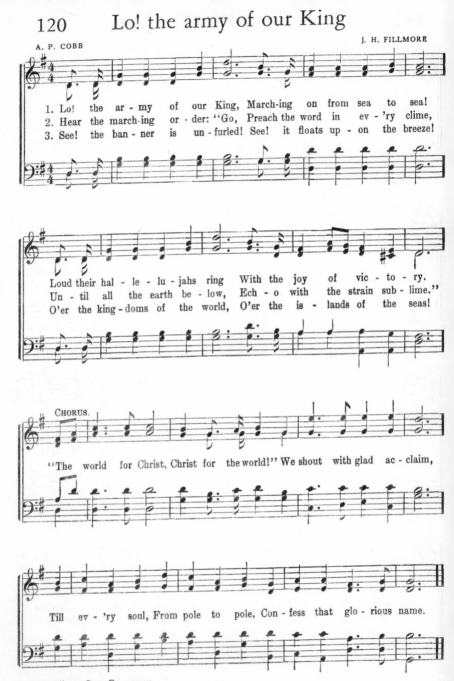

1. Lo! the ar - my of our King, March-ing on from sea to sea!
2. Hear the march-ing or - der: "Go, Preach the word in ev - 'ry clime,
3. See! the ban - ner is un - furled! See! it floats up - on the breeze!

Loud their hal - le - lu - jahs ring With the joy of vic - to - ry.
Un - til all the earth be - low, Ech - o with the strain sub - lime."
O'er the king - doms of the world, O'er the is - lands of the seas!

CHORUS.

"The world for Christ, Christ for the world!" We shout with glad ac - claim,

Till ev - 'ry soul, From pole to pole, Con - fess that glo - rious name.

121 Lead on, O King Eternal

ERNEST W. SHURTLEFF

HENRY SMART

1. Lead on, O King E-ter-nal, The day of march has come;
2. Lead on, O King E-ter-nal, Till sin's fierce war shall cease,
3. Lead on, O King E-ter-nal, We fol-low, not with fears,

Hence-forth in fields of con-quest Thy tents shall be our home;
And ho-li-ness shall whis-per The sweet A-men of peace;
For glad-ness breaks like morn-ing Wher-e'er Thy face ap-pears;

Thru days of prep-a-ra-tion Thy grace has made us strong,
For not with swords, loud clash-ing, Nor roll of stir-ring drums,
Thy cross is lift-ed o'er us; We jour-ney in its light;

And now, O King E-ter-nal, We lift our bat-tle song.
With deeds of love and mer-cy, The heaven-ly king-dom comes.
The crown a-waits the con-quest; Lead on, O God of Might.

122　My Peace I Leave with Thee

GERALDINE D. ROBINSON

ARR. FROM WEBER

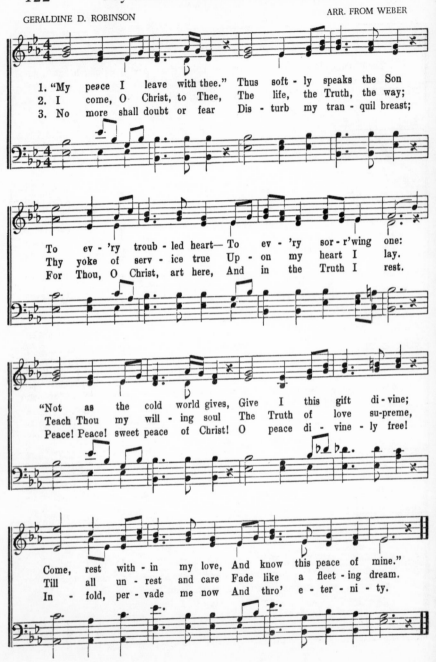

1. "My peace I leave with thee." Thus soft-ly speaks the Son
2. I come, O Christ, to Thee, The life, the Truth, the way;
3. No more shall doubt or fear Dis-turb my tran-quil breast;

To ev-'ry troub-led heart— To ev-'ry sor-r'wing one:
Thy yoke of serv-ice true Up-on my heart I lay.
For Thou, O Christ, art here, And in the Truth I rest.

"Not as the cold world gives, Give I this gift di-vine;
Teach Thou my will-ing soul The Truth of love su-preme,
Peace! Peace! sweet peace of Christ! O peace di-vine-ly free!

Come, rest with-in my love, And know this peace of mine."
Till all un-rest and care Fade like a fleet-ing dream.
In-fold, per-vade me now And thro' e-ter-ni-ty.

123 We come to Thee, O Lord

ADAM GEIBEL

We come to Thee, O Lord, in si - lent pray'r; Our hearts to Thee, Our

hearts to Thee Are o - pen... now.... A - men, A - men.

124 Break Thou the bread of life

MARY A. LATHBURY

WM. F. SHERWIN

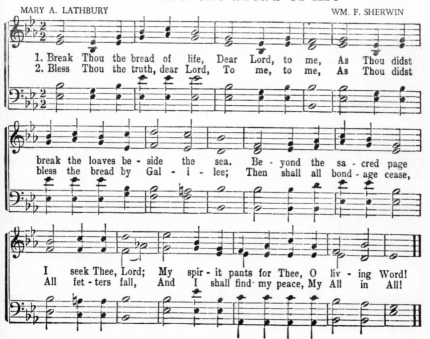

1. Break Thou the bread of life, Dear Lord, to me, As Thou didst
2. Bless Thou the truth, dear Lord, To me, to me, As Thou didst

break the loaves be - side the sea. Be - yond the sa - cred page
bless the bread by Gal - i - lee; Then shall all bond - age cease,

I seek Thee, Lord; My spir - it pants for Thee, O liv - ing Word!
All fet - ters fall, And I shall find· my peace, My All in All!

125 My Father is rich in houses and lands

HATTIE E. BUELL

JOHN B. SUMNER

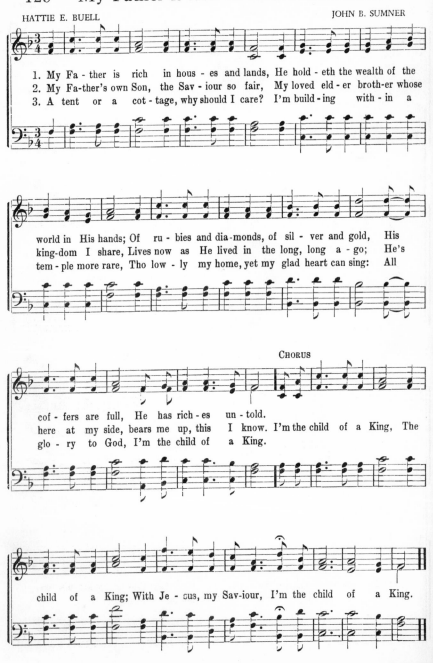

1. My Fa - ther is rich in hous - es and lands, He hold - eth the wealth of the
2. My Fa - ther's own Son, the Sav - iour so fair, My loved eld - er broth - er whose
3. A tent or a cot - tage, why should I care? I'm build - ing with - in a

world in His hands; Of ru - bies and dia - monds, of sil - ver and gold, His
king - dom I share, Lives now as He lived in the long, long a - go; He's
tem - ple more rare, Tho low - ly my home, yet my glad heart can sing: All

CHORUS

cof - fers are full, He has rich - es un - told.
here at my side, bears me up, this I know. I'm the child of a King, The
glo - ry to God, I'm the child of a King.

child of a King; With Je - sus, my Sav - iour, I'm the child of a King.

126 I know I love Thee better Lord

FRANCES R. HAVERGAL

R. E. HUDSON

1. I know I love Thee bet - ter, Lord, Than a - ny earth - ly joy,
2. I know that Thou art near - er still, Than a - ny earth - ly throng;
3. Thou hast put glad - ness in my heart; Then well may I re - joice!

For Thou hast giv - en me the peace, Which noth - ing can de - stroy.
And sweet - er is the tho't of Thee, Than a - ny love - ly song.
And in the se - cret of Thy love I praise Thee with my voice.

CHORUS

The half has nev - er yet been told, Of love so full and free;
yet been told,

The half has nev - er yet been told, Thy life— it cleans-eth me.
yet been told,

127 Love lifted me

JAMES ROWE

HOWARD E. SMITH

1. I was sink - ing deep in sin, Far from the peace - ful shore,
2. All my heart to Him I give, Ev - er to Him I'll cling,
3. Souls in dan - ger, look a - bove, Je - sus com - plete - ly saves;

Ver - y deep - ly stained with - in, Sink - ing to rise no more;
In His bless - ed pres - ence live, Ev - er His prais - es sing;
He will lift you by His love Out of the an - gry waves;

But the Mas - ter of the sea Heard my de - spair - ing cry,
Love so might - y and so true Mer - its my soul's best songs;
He's the Mas - ter of the sea, Bil - lows His will o - bey;

From the wa - ters lift - ed me, Now safe am I.
Faith - ful, lov - ing serv - ice, too, To Him be - longs.
He your Sav - iour wants to be— Be saved to - day.

CHORUS

Love lift - ed me! .... Love lift - ed me! .... When noth - ing
e - ven me! e - ven me!

Love lifted me

else could help, Love lift-ed me; Love lift-ed me! . . . .
e - ven me!

Love lift-ed me! . . . . When noth-ing else could help, Love lift-ed me.
e - ven me!

128   Love lifted me

1 I was searching all about,
  Seeking for life and peace,
Thinking they were found with-
    out,
  Still I could find no ease;
But the Christ who dwells in me
  Heard my despairing cry,
Said, "Why seek outside of Thee,
  For here am I."

Chorus.

Love lifted me, Love lifted me,
  From thots of doubt and strife,
    Love lifted me.
Love lifted me, Love lifted me,
  With Christ—eternal life,
    Love lifted me.

2 All my heart to Him I give,
  Ever to Him I'll cling,
In His blessed presence live,
  Ever His praises sing.

Love so mighty and so true
  Merits my soul's best songs,
Faithful, loving service, too,
  To Him belongs.

3 Spirit substance everywhere,
  Waiting for us to mold;
With Christ Jesus we can share
  Treasures of worth untold.
Words and thoughts have molding
    power,
  So let us careful be,
Knowing that we're building our
  Eternity.

Chorus for last verse.

Love lifteth me, Love lifteth me,
  From thots of want and lack,
    Love lifteth me.
Love prospers me, Love prospers
    me,
  Love thots we send out, come back
    Prosperity.

129 Inheritance

IRENE STANLEY

GEO. MARKS EVANS

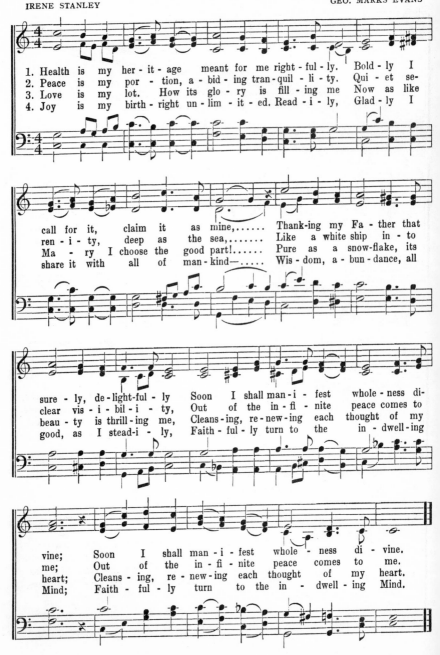

1. Health is my her - it - age meant for me right - ful - ly. Bold - ly I
2. Peace is my por - tion, a - bid - ing tran - quil - li - ty. Qui - et se-
3. Love is my lot. How its glo - ry is fill - ing me Now as like
4. Joy is my birth - right un - lim - it - ed. Read - i - ly, Glad - ly I

call for it, claim it as mine,...... Thank-ing my Fa - ther that
ren - i - ty, deep as the sea,....... Like a white ship in - to
Ma - ry I choose the good part!...... Pure as a snow-flake, its
share it with all of man-kind—..... Wis - dom, a - bun - dance, all

sure - ly, de - light-ful - ly Soon I shall man - i - fest whole - ness di -
clear vis - i - bil - i - ty, Out of the in - fi - nite peace comes to
beau - ty is thrill-ing me, Cleans-ing, re - new-ing each thought of my
good, as I stead-i - ly, Faith - ful - ly turn to the in - dwell-ing

vine; Soon I shall man - i - fest whole - ness di - vine.
me; Out of the in - fi - nite peace comes to me.
heart; Cleans - ing, re - new-ing each thought of my heart.
Mind; Faith - ful - ly turn to the in - dwell - ing Mind.

130 Thou art the way to Thee alone

GEORGE W. DOANE

THOMAS A. ARNE

1. Thou art the Way: to Thee a - lone From sin and death we flee;
2. Thou art the Truth: Thy word a - lone True wis - dom can im - part;
3. Thou art the Life: the rend - ing tomb Pro - claims Thy con - q'ring arm,
4. Thou art the Way, the Truth, the Life: Grant us that way to know,

And he who would the Fa - ther seek Must seek Him, Lord, by Thee.
Thou on - ly canst in - form the mind, And pur - i - fy the heart.
And those who put their trust in Thee Nor death nor hell shall harm.
That Truth to keep, that Life to win, Whose joys e - ter - nal flow.

131 Since Jesus is my friend

Tr. CATHERINE WINKWORTH

JOSEPH E. SWEETSER

1. Since Je - sus is my friend, And I to Him be - long,
2. He whis - pers in my breast Sweet words of ho - ly cheer;
3. My heart for glad - ness springs, It can not more be sad;
4. The sun that lights mine eyes Is Christ, the Lord, a - bove:

It mat - ters not what foes in - tend, How - ev - er fierce and strong.
How they who seek in God their rest Shall ev - er find Him near.
For ver - y joy it laughs and sings, Sees naught but sun - shine glad.
I sing for joy for that which lies Stored up for me in love.

In tender compassion

L. E. J.

L. E. JONES

1. In ten - der com - pas - sion and won - der - ful love, The
2. His arm is a - bun - dant - ly a - ble to save, His
3. No need have I ev - er to troub - le my breast, Or

Fa - ther looks down from on high; He know - eth the ra - ven hath
eye is a guide to my feet; Since love sought and found me, I
fear what the mor - row may bring; The heart of the Fa - ther is

need of its food, And hear - eth in mer - cy its cry.
con - stant - ly dwell With Him in com - pan - ion - ship sweet.
plan - ning my way, And I am the child of a King.

CHORUS

The ra - ven He feed - eth, then why should I fear, To the heart of the

Fa - ther His chil - dren are dear; So, if the way dark - ens or

In tender compassion

storms gath - er o'er, I'll sim - ply look up - ward and trust Him the more.

133　Sweet bells of heaven

MARY E. BUTTERS

CLARA H. SCOTT

1. Sweet bells of heav'n, how glad ye ring, Of heav'n-ly Love, our new-born King!
2. Sweet bells of heav'n, ye are a song, Pæ - an of praise, the whole day long!
3. I hear the mys - tic puls - es fall Of One Great Heart that beats for all;

Deep-toned and pure and true as steel, Ye touch on chords that
When list - 'ning in the si - lence sweet, I catch the foot - falls
From low - ly peas - ant, prince, to King, Sweet bells of heav'n, for

Ye touch on
I catch the
Sweet Lells of

rit.

bind and heal, Ye touch on chords that bind and heal.
of Christ's feet, I catch the foot falls of Christ's feet.
ev - er ring! Sweet bells of heav'n, for - ev - er ring!

chords that bind and heal, Ye touch on chords, ye touch on chords that bind and heal.
foot - falls of Christ's feet, I catch the gen - tle, gen - tle foot-falls of Christ's feet
heav'n, for - ev - er ring, Sweet bells of heav'n, sweet bells of heav'n, for - ev - er ring.

134   O Little Town of Bethlehem

PHILLIPS BROOKS

LEWIS H. REDNER

1. O lit - tle town of Beth - le - hem, How still we see thee lie;
2. For Christ is born of Ma - ry; And gath - ered all a - bove,
3. How si - lent - ly, how si - lent - ly, The won - drous gift is giv'n!
4. O ho - ly Child of Beth - le - hem, De - scend on us, we pray;

A - bove thy deep and dream - less sleep The si - lent stars go by:
While mor - tals sleep, the an - gels keep Their watch of won - d'ring love.
So God im - parts to hu - man hearts The bless - ings of His heav'n.
Cast out our sin, and en - ter in, Be born in us to - day.

Yet in thy dark streets shin - eth The ev - er - last - ing Light;
O morn - ing stars, to - geth - er Pro - claim the ho - ly birth;
No ear may hear His com - ing, But in this world of sin,
We hear the Christ - mas an - gels The great glad ti - dings tell;

The hopes and fears of all the years Are met in thee to - night.
And prais - es sing to God the King, And peace to men on earth.
Where meek souls will re - ceive Him still, The dear Christ en - ters in.
O come to us, a - bide with us, Our Lord Em - man - u - el.

135 It came upon the midnight clear

EDWIN H. SEARS

R. S. WILLIS

1. It came up - on the mid - night clear, That glo - rious song of old,
2. Still thru the clo - ven skies they come, With peace - ful wings un - furled,
3. For lo! the days are hasten - ing on, By proph - et - bards fore - told,

From an - gels bend - ing near the earth, To touch their harps of gold;
And still ce - les - tial mu - sic floats O'er all the wea - ry world;
When with the ev - er - cir - cling years Comes round the age of gold!

"Peace to the earth, good-will to men, From heav'n's all-gra - cious King;"
A - bove its sad and low - ly plains, They bend on heav'n - ly wing,
When peace shall o - ver all the earth Its fi - nal splen - dors fling,

The earth in sol - emn still - ness lay, To hear the an - gels sing.
And ev - er o'er its Ba - bel sounds, The bless - ed an - gels sing.
And the whole world send back the song Which now the an - gels sing.

Christmas Praise

FRANCIS J. GABLE

FRANGKISER

1. My soul doth mag - ni - fy the Lord, My spir - it is re - joic - ing;
2. The new - born Babe at Beth - le - hem Re - news the old, old sto - ry;
3. My soul doth mag - ni - fy the Lord For price - less gift of liv - ing,

Good will and peace to all man - kind My hap - py heart is voic - ing.
His Spir - it lives a - gain in me And fills my life with glo - ry.
And for the Christ that teach - es me To know the joy of liv - ing.

CHORUS

Glo - ry to God, glo - ry to God,

This is the glad re - frain; ....

Glo - ry to God, glo - ry to God, . . .

Christmas Praise

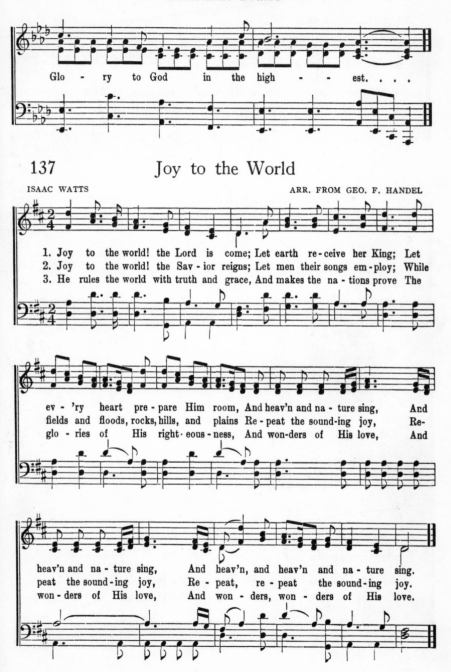

Glo - ry to God in the high - - est. . . .

137　　　Joy to the World

ISAAC WATTS　　　　　　　　　　　　ARR. FROM GEO. F. HANDEL

1. Joy to the world! the Lord is come; Let earth re-ceive her King; Let
2. Joy to the world! the Sav-ior reigns; Let men their songs em-ploy; While
3. He rules the world with truth and grace, And makes the na - tions prove The

ev - 'ry heart pre-pare Him room, And heav'n and na - ture sing, And
fields and floods, rocks, hills, and plains Re - peat the sound-ing joy, Re-
glo - ries of His right-eous-ness, And won-ders of His love, And

heav'n and na - ture sing, And heav'n, and heav'n and na - ture sing.
peat the sound-ing joy, Re - peat, re - peat the sound-ing joy.
won - ders of His love, And won - ders, won - ders of His love.

A Christmas Greeting

VIVIAN YEISER LARAMORE   FRANGKISER

1. Be - hold the star, the won-drous star That leads to Christ in you!
2. Up - on this day His love su-preme Re - lights the in - ner flame,

The wise have fol - lowed from a - far And found the prom - ise true.
And we who walked as in a dream A - wake to know His name;

Oh, let the bells in rap - ture ring And peace its joy im - part;
For He is here whom we a - dore, Oh, hap - py tho't and sweet!

For He is come who shall be king: The Christ in ev - 'ry heart.
For - ev - er and for - ev - er - more The Christ in you I greet.

139   Silent Night! Holiest Night!

JOSEPH MOHR

FRANZ GRUBER

1. Si - lent night! ho - li - est night! All is dark save the light
2. Si - lent night! ho - li - est night! Dark-ness flies, all is light:
3. Si - lent night! ho - li - est night! Won-drous Star, lend thy light;

Yon - der where they sweet vig - il keep O'er the Babe, who in si - lent sleep,
Shep-herds hear the an - gels sing: "Al - le - lu - ia! hail the King!
With the an - gels let us sing Al - le - lu - ia to our King!

Rests in heav - en - ly peace, Rests in heav - en - ly peace.
Christ the Sav - ior is here, Je - sus the Sav - ior is here."
Christ the Sav - ior is here, Je - sus the Sav - ior is here.

Holy light! perfect light!
Christ of God, oh, how bright
Doth thy Spirit shine alway!
Healing, blessing man each day
With thy heavenly love,
With thy heavenly love.

upper - Trumpet
Lower Adjust no0
0044 15213
Percussion - On - Third
Foot 1,4.

140 Hark the herald angels sing

CHARLES WESLEY

MENDELSSOHN

1. Hark! the her - ald an - gels sing, "Glo - ry to the new - born King,
2. See, He lays His glo - ry by, Born that man no more may die;

Peace on earth, and mer - cy mild, God and sin - ners rec - on - ciled!"
Born to raise the sons of earth; Born to give them sec - ond birth.

Joy - ful all ye na - tions, rise; Join the tri - umph of the skies;
Let us, then, with an - gels sing, "Glo - ry to the new - born King!

With th'an - gel - ic host pro - claim, Christ is born in Beth - le - hem!
Peace on earth, and mer - cy mild, God and sin - ners rec - on - ciled!

With th'an - gel - ic host pro - claim, Christ is born in Beth - le - hem!
Peace on earth, and mer - cy mild, God and sin - ners rec - on - ciled!"

141 'Neath the stars a song is ringing

J. L. H. Arr. from "Humoresque," by ANTON DVORAK

1. 'Neath the stars a song is ring-ing, Ech-oes far and wide are wing-ing,
2. 'Neath the stars resounds the sto-ry Of the Lord, the King of glo-ry;

Cho.—'Neath the stars a Babe is sleep-ing, Maid-en moth-er vig-il keep-ing,

Float-ing o'er the tran-quil, dreaming plain; Waft-ed down from star-ry por-tal,
Come to earth from heaven's gates of gold; Wondrous love, all love ex-cell-ing,

Un-seen an-gels hov'ring o'er His rest; Tho He lies in man-ger low-ly,

FINE.

Tid-ings sweet of joy im-mor-tal, List! O list the glad re-frain!
Lo! the Lord with man is dwell-ing; Seek the Prince of Peace fore-told.

Yet the Son of God most ho-ly, Prince of Peace thru a-ges blest.

SOP. AND ALTO. In Parts, faster.

Seek Him, O seek Him, haste in the starlight, Haste 'neath the glories guiding on;
Seek Him, O seek Him, Monarch, Redeem-er, Bright o'er His rest the splendors fall;

rit. D. C.

Seek Him, O seek Him, glad homage bringing, Ye shall find the roy-al One.
Seek Him, O seek Him, scep-ter e-ter-nal, King of kings and Lord of all.

The music the property of Hall-Mack Co.

142 Royal Babe in rest so lowly

E. D. Y.

I. OFFENBACH. Arr. by ALFRED JUDSON

1. Roy - al Babe, in rest so low - ly, We would seek Thy man-ger; Son of God and
2. Roy - al Babe fore-told thru a - ges, Come to earth a stran-ger; Sung by an - gels,

SOP. AND ALTO. *Parts.*

King most ho - ly, Lord of life and light. Ser-aphs sang 'mid star - ry splendor,
sought by sag - es, Promised Prince Di-vine! Still a - far the anthems ringing,

Of Thy pow'r and glo - ry; We our joy - ous praise would ren - der,
Her - ald Thine ap - pear - ing; Bright Thy star, its glo - ries fling - ing,

SOP. AND ALTO, OR ALL.
Unison.
ALL *Parts*

'Neath the stars so bright; Hail to Thee! Hail to Thee! Lord of all!
O'er our path shall shine; Hail to Thee! Hail to Thee! Lord of all!

CHORUS.

Roy - al One, O Lord of glo - ry, Come in low - ly guise! We would sing Thy

Royal Babe in rest so lowly

MALE VOICES

wondrous sto-ry, 'Neath the starry skies! Welcome, O heav-en-ly Guest,

SOP. AND ALTO.   ALL. *Parts.*

Welcome Re-deem-er so blest! Praise with joy we sing, We hail our King!

143   Glory be to the Father

GREATOREX

Glo-ry be to the Fa-ther, and to the Son, and to the

Ho-ly Ghost; As it was in the be-gin-ning, is

now, and ev-er shall be, World with-out end. A-men. A-men.

144 O Come all ye faithful

Tr. F. OAKELEY

Anonymous

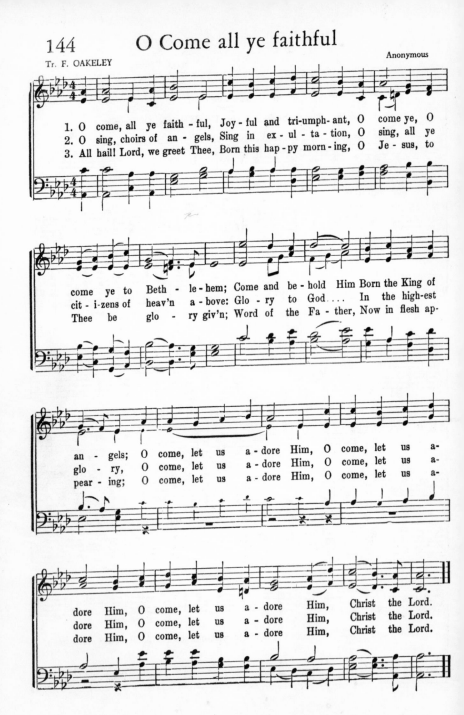

1. O come, all ye faith-ful, Joy-ful and tri-umph-ant, O come ye, O
2. O sing, choirs of an - gels, Sing in ex-ul - ta - tion, O sing, all ye
3. All hail! Lord, we greet Thee, Born this hap-py morn-ing, O Je - sus, to

come ye to Beth - le-hem; Come and be-hold Him Born the King of
cit - i-zens of heav'n a - bove: Glo - ry to God.... In the high-est
Thee be glo - ry giv'n; Word of the Fa - ther, Now in flesh ap-

an - gels; O come, let us a - dore Him, O come, let us a-
glo - ry, O come, let us a - dore Him, O come, let us a-
pear - ing; O come, let us a - dore Him, O come, let us a-

dore Him, O come, let us a - dore Him, Christ the Lord.
dore Him, O come, let us a - dore Him, Christ the Lord.
dore Him, O come, let us a - dore Him, Christ the Lord.

145   New mercies new blessings

1 New mercies, new blessings, new light on thy way;
New courage, new hope, and new strength for each day;
New notes of thanksgiving, new chords of delight;
New praise in the morning, new songs in the night,
New praise in the morning, new songs in the night.

2 New wine in thy chalice, new altars to raise;
New fruits for thy Master, new garments of praise;
New gifts from His treasures, new smiles from His face;
New streams from the fountain of infinite grace,
New streams from the fountain of infinite grace.

3 New stars for thy crown and new tokens of love;
New gleams of the glory that shines from above;
New light of His countenance, full and unpriced.
All this be the joy of thy new life in Christ,
All this be the joy of thy new life in Christ.

146   Holy holy holy

W. F. SHERWIN

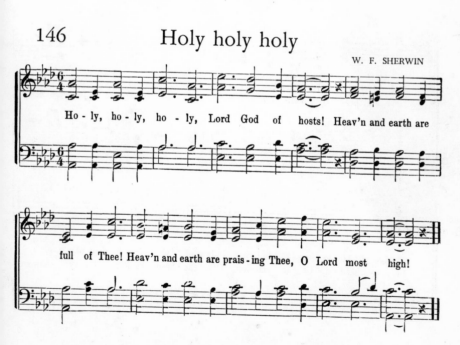

Ho-ly, ho-ly, ho-ly, Lord God of hosts! Heav'n and earth are full of Thee! Heav'n and earth are prais-ing Thee, O Lord most high!

147 Hark the sound of holy voices

C. WORDSWORTH

J. B. DYKES

1. Hark! the sound of ho - ly voic - es, Chant-ing at the crys - tal sea,
2. Now they reign in heav'n-ly glo - ry, Now they walk in gold - en light,

Al - le - lu - ia, Al - le - lu - ia, Al - le - lu - ia, Lord to Thee:
Now they drink, as from a riv - er, Ho - ly bliss and in - fi - nite:

cres.

Mul - ti - tude which none can num - ber, Like the stars in glo - ry stands,
Love and peace they taste for - ev - er, And all truth and knowl-edge see

rall.

Clothed in white ap- par - el, hold-ing Palms of vic - t'ry in their hands.
In the be - a - tif - ic vis - ion Of the bless - ed Trin - i - ty. A-men.

148   Come ye thankful people

HENRY ALFORD

G. J. ELVEY

1. Come, ye thank-ful peo - ple, come, Raise the song of har - vest-home;
2. All the world is God's own field, Fruit un - to His praise to yield;
3. For the Lord our God shall come, And shall take His har - vest home;

All is safe - ly gath - ered in, Ere the win - ter storms be - gin;
Wheat and tares to - geth - er sown, Un - to joy or sor - row grown;
From His field shall in that day All of - fen - ces purge a - way;

God, our Ma - ker, doth pro - vide For our wants to be sup - plied;
First the blade, and then the ear, Then the full corn shall ap - pear:
There, for - ev - er pur - i - fied, In His pres - ence to a - bide—

Come to God's own tem - ple, come, Raise the song of har - vest-home.
Lord of har - vest, grant that we Whole-some grain and pure may be.
E - ven so, Lord, quick-ly come, Raise the glo - rious har - vest-home.

149 America the Beautiful

KATHERINE LEE BATES

SAMUEL A. WARD

1. O beau - ti - ful for spa - cious skies, For am - ber waves of grain,
2. O beau - ti - ful for pil - grim feet, Whose stern, im - pas-sioned stress
3. O beau - ti - ful for he - roes proved In lib - er - at - ing strife,
4. O beau - ti - ful for pa - triot dream That sees be - yond the years,

For pur - ple moun-tain maj - es - ties A - bove the fruit - ed plain!
A thor - ough-fare for free - dom beat A - cross the wil - der - ness!
Who more than self their coun - try loved, And mer - cy more than life!
Thine al - a - bas - ter cit - ies gleam, Undimmed by hu - man tears!

A - mer - i - ca! A - mer - i - ca! God shed His grace on thee,
A - mer - i - ca! A - mer - i - ca! God mend thine ev - 'ry flaw,
A - mer - i - ca! A - mer - i - ca! May God thy gold re - fine,
A - mer - i - ca! A - mer - i - ca! God shed His grace on thee,

And crown thy good with broth - er - hood From sea to shin - ing sea!
Con - firm thy soul in self - con - trol, Thy lib - er - ty in law!
Till all suc - cess be no - ble - ness, And ev - 'ry gain di - vine!
And crown thy good with broth - er - hood From sea to shin - ing sea!

150 My country 'tis of thee

S. F. SMITH

H. CAREY

1. My coun-try! 'tis of thee, Sweet land of lib-er-ty,
2. My na-tive coun-try, thee—Land of the no-ble, free—
3. Let mu-sic swell the breeze, And ring from all the trees
4. Our fa-thers' God! to Thee, Au-thor of lib-er-ty,

Of thee I sing: Land where my fa-thers died, Land of the
Thy name I love; I love thy rocks and rills, Thy woods and
Sweet free-dom's song; Let mor-tal tongues a-wake, Let all that
To Thee we sing: Long may our land be bright With free-dom's

pil-grims' pride, From ev-'ry moun-tain side Let free-dom ring!
tem-pled hills; My heart with rap-ture thrills, Like that a-bove.
breathe par-take; Let rocks their si-lence break, The sound pro-long.
ho-ly light; Pro-tect us by Thy might, Great God, our King!

151 Our Father God to Thee

1 Our Father, God, to Thee,
   Throughout eternity,
      Thy name we praise!
   Thou art the Source of all;
   Thou lovest great and small;
   Thy life sustaineth all;
      Thine be the praise!

2 I am Thy child of health;
   I am Thy heir of wealth;
      All Thine is mine,
   Joy and prosperity
   Are ever mine in Thee,
   Wisdom and harmony
      And Love Divine.

152 All the air with joy is rife

LYRA DAVIDICA

1. All the air with joy is rife, Al - le - lu - ia!
2. Morn of glo - ry— no al - loy, Al - le - lu - ia.
3. Let no earth - ly dis - cord glide, Al - le - lu - ia.

Spring - ing life from death is born; Al - le - lu - ia!
Can thy match - less splen - dor dim; Al - le - lu - ia!
Thru the grand up - swell - ing lay; Al - le - lu - ia!

Plas - tic na - ture feels the strife, Al - le - lu - ia!
Sing, O heart, thy song of joy— Al - le - lu - ia!
Sing, O hearts, what - e'er be - tide, Al - le - lu - ia!

'Tis the res - ur - rec - tion morn, Al - le - lu - ia!
Sing thy great tri - umph - al hymn, Al - le - lu - ia!
For the Lord is ris'n to - day. Al - le - lu - ia!

153 No more thought of dark and gloom

1 No more thought of dark and gloom, Alleluia;
No more thought of death and tomb, Alleluia;
To the heavens and the lights, Alleluia;
Let your soul ascend the heights, Alleluia.

2 Out of discord and of strife, Alleluia;
To the consciousness of life, Alleluia;
Take Thy place, O radiant Son, Alleluia;
By Thy Father, heavenly One, Alleluia.

3 By Thy dazzling, radiant rays, Alleluia;
Shine, illuminate Thy days, Alleluia;
Constant be, the truth will dawn, Alleluia;
Man arise! ascend! shine on, Alleluia. Amen.

154 O the joy to feel and know

ELEANOR ALLEN SCHROLL

LOUIS LE SAINT

1. O the joy to feel and know, Eyes di-vine are heed-ing; Sweetest bless-ings
2. O the love that saves and keeps Wayward souls from fall-ing; O the love that
3. O the hope I feel to-day, O the peace of know-ing; He will lead me

CHORUS.

to be-stow, When His help I'm need-ing.
nev-er sleeps, Hears His chil-dren call-ing. O the joy to feel Him near,
all the way, For I'm no-bler grow-ing.

True and constant ev-er; What have I to doubt or fear? Je-sus fails me nev-er.

155 Eternal Life Is Here

ARRANGED BY J. H. F.

1. E - ter - nal life is here! Sus - tain - ing pow - er! A ra - diant
2. E - ter - nal life is here! That life is won-drous love! My life is
3. E - ter - nal life is here! I've sown this pre-cious seed, And now I

light to me, a heav'n-ly dow - er. E - ter - nal life is here!
cen-tered in the life of God. E - ter - nal life is here!
feel its pow'r in word and deed. E - ter - nal life is here!

O what a won-drous tho't! A might-y truth to me these words have taught.
I rest in joy and peace; And as I live in God, all joys in - crease.
This life is full and free! The dawn-ing light of Truth I clear - ly see.

156 Be Ye Doers of the Word

J. H. FILLMORE

Be ye do - ers of the word, And not hear - ers on - ly;

Be ye do - ers of the word, And not hear - ers on - ly.

157 He is risen He is risen

MRS. C. F. ALEXANDER

CHAS. M. FILLMORE

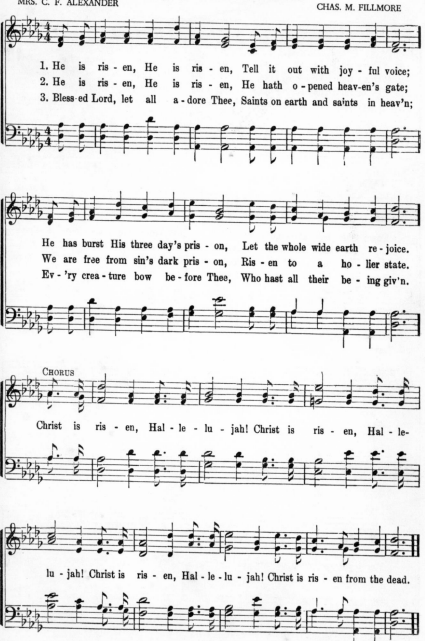

1. He is ris-en, He is ris-en, Tell it out with joy-ful voice;
2. He is ris-en, He is ris-en, He hath o-pened heav-en's gate;
3. Bless-ed Lord, let all a-dore Thee, Saints on earth and saints in heav'n;

He has burst His three day's pris-on, Let the whole wide earth re-joice.
We are free from sin's dark pris-on, Ris-en to a ho-lier state.
Ev-'ry crea-ture bow be-fore Thee, Who hast all their be-ing giv'n.

CHORUS

Christ is ris-en, Hal-le-lu-jah! Christ is ris-en, Hal-le-

lu-jah! Christ is ris-en, Hal-le-lu-jah! Christ is ris-en from the dead.

158 There shall be showers of blessing

D. W. WHITTLE

JAMES McGRANAHAN

1. "There shall be show-ers of bless-ing:" This is the prom-ise of love;
2. "There shall be show-ers of bless-ing"— Pre-cious re-viv-ing a-gain;
3. "There shall be show-ers of bless-ing," Send them up-on us, O Lord;
4. "There shall be show-ers of bless-ing:" O that to-day they might fall,

There shall be sea-sons re-fresh-ing, Sent from the Sav-iour a-bove.
O - ver the hills and the val-leys, Sound of a - bun-dance of rain.
Grant to us now a re-fresh-ing, Come, and now hon - or Thy Word.
Now as to God we're con-fess-ing, Now as on Je - sus we call!

CHORUS

Show - - ers of bless - ing, Show-ers of bless-ing we need;
Show-ers, show-ers

Mer - cy-drops round us are fall - ing, But for the show-ers we plead.

159 Now are the showers of blessings

1 Now are the showers of blessings
    Sent by the Father of love;
  Now is the time of expressing
    Bountiful gifts from above.

Chorus.—Showers of blessings,
    Showers of blessings in store;
  Windows of heaven are open,
    Showers of blessings outpour.

2 Now are the showers of blessings,
    Meeting our momently need;
  Now are the riches of heaven
    Healing our hearts of all greed.

3 Bountiful measure fulfilling,
    Pouring upon us, O Lord!
  Now are the showers of blessings,
    Promises made by Thy Word.

160 Thou must be true thyself

HORATIUS BONAR

E. JOSEPHINE TROUP

1. Thou must be true thy - self If thou the true wouldst teach;
2. Think tru - ly, and thy thots Shall the world's fam - ine feed;

Thy soul must o - ver - flow if thou An - oth - er's soul wouldst reach:
Speak tru - ly, and each word of thine Shall be a fruit - ful seed;

The o - ver - flow of heart it needs To give the lips full speech.
Live tru - ly, and thy life shall be A great and no - ble creed.

161 Father in heaven

RUDYARD KIPLING

TIMOTHY R. MATTHEWS

1. Fa - ther in heav'n, who lov - est all, O help Thy chil - dren when they call,
2. Teach us to rule our - selves al - way, Controlled and clean - ly night and day,
3. Teach us to look in all our ends On Thee for Judge and not our friends,
4. Teach us de - light in sim - ple things, And mirth that has no bit - ter springs,

That they may build from age to age An un - de - fil - ed her - i - tage.
That we may bring, if need a - rise, No maimed or worthless sac - ri - fice.
That we, with Thee, may walk un - cowed By fear or fa - vor of the crowd.
For - give-ness free of e - vil done, And love to all men 'neath the sun.

162 I would be true

HAROLD ARNOLD WATERS

JOSEPH YATES PEEK

1. I would be true, for there are those who trust me; I would be
2. I would be friend of all— the foe, the friend - less; I would be

pure, for there are those who care; I would be strong, for
giv - ing, and for - get the gift; I would be hum - ble,

I would be true

there is much to suf - fer; I would be brave, for there is
for I know my weak - ness; I would look up, and laugh, and

much to dare, I would be brave, for there is much to dare.
love, and lift, I would look up, and laugh, and love, and lift.

163   **Be Still, and Know**

MRS. J. O. GILBERT

EDWARD DIDDLE

1. "Be still, and know." Oh, bless - ed words! This mes - sage from the Lord of Lords
2. "Be still, and know" e - ter - nal peace And har - mo-nies that nev - er cease.
3. "Be still, and know" a - bun - dant store Is yours in heav'n for-ev - er-more.
4. "Be still, and know" you're Spir-it, free, Have al - ways been, will al - ways be;

Un - meas-ured joy and peace af-fords: "Be still, and know that I am God."
With faith that ev - er must in-crease "Be still, and know that I am God."
With joy - ous grat - i - tude a - dore—"Be still, and know that I am God."
Right now you're in e - ter - ni - ty. "Be still, and know that I am God."

164 He that dwelleth in the silent

INEZ RUSSELL

JOHN ZUNDEL

1. He that dwell-eth in the si-lent, Se-cret place of God, Most High,
2. Tho by day the ar-row fli-eth; Tho by night the ter-ror stalks;
3. Thou, Je-ho-vah, art my ref-uge! Thou my ha-bi-ta-tion art!
4. The young li-on and the ser-pent I shall tram-ple un-der foot.

Shall a-bide with-in His shad-ow Peace-ful, un-a-fraid, se-cure.
Tho the pes-ti-lence in dark-ness; Tho de-struc-tion wastes a-way;
There no e-vil shall be-fall me, Nor shall plague come nigh my tent.
I have set my love up-on Thee And Thou wilt de-liv-er me.

For Je-ho-vah is my ref-uge, And my God in whom I trust;
Tho ten thou-sand fall be-side me, Un-a-fraid I stand with Thee,
O-ver me, O great Je-ho-vah, Thou wilt give Thy an-gels charge,
I have known Thy name, Je-ho-vah, And Thou set-teth me on high.

Hides me 'neath His spreading pin-ions, Girds me with His ho-ly truth.
Know-ing that be-neath Thy shad-ow In that se-cret place I stand.
They will shel-ter me and keep me; Bear me up in ten-der hands.
Sat-is-fied with life a-bund-ant, Thy sal-va-tion shall I see. A-men.

165 In the Garden

C. A. M.

C. AUSTIN MILES

1. I come to the gar-den a - lone, While the dew is still on the ros - es; And the voice I hear, Fall - ing on my ear; The Son of God dis - clos - es.

2. He speaks, and the sound of His voice Is so sweet the birds hush their sing - ing, And the mel - o - dy, That He gave to me; With - in my heart is ring - ing.

3. I'd stay in the gar-den with Him Tho the night a - round me be fall - ing, But He bids me go; Thru the voice of woe, His voice to me is call - ing.

CHORUS.

And He walks with me, and He talks with me, And He tells me I am His own, And the joy we share as we tar - ry there, None oth - er has ev - er known.

166   I See Abundance Everywhere

THEODOSIA SMITH

JNO. R. SWENEY

1. I see a-bun-dance ev-'ry-where, God's rich sup-ply be-yond com-pare;
2. I pray that I may ev-er be In sweet com-mun-ion, Lord, with Thee.
3. There is no lack! All-boun-ti-ful, His love pro-vides. How beau-ti-ful

'Tis ours to use and to en-joy, His gift to us, with-out al-loy.
Up-held, pro-tect-ed by Thy hand, Se-cure in Thy dear care I stand.
To know God guides us on our way, Sus-tains and bless-es us each day!

CHORUS

Pros-per-i-ty, pros-per-i-ty, I know my own shall come to me.

God sends His chil-dren joy and peace, Good health and wis-dom and in-crease,

And we our grate-ful voic-es raise To Thee, O God, in hymns of praise.

167 Prosperity

FRANCIS J. GABLE

FRANGKISER

1. From the Fa-ther's store Rich-es now out-pour For the one who
2. Heav-en's door is wide; And the end-less tide Of the Fa-ther's
3. By His law we live, And we free-ly give Of the good that

will be-lieve, Who can un-der-stand From His o-pen hand
love and wealth Flows, a might-y stream, On whose wa-ters gleam
God be-stows. Thus a rich sup-ply Of His wealth is nigh,

CHORUS

Come the bless-ings we re-ceive.......
True pros-per-i-ty and health...... I am pros-pered,
For our need the Fa-ther knows. .....

Tru-ly pros-pered, By His lov-ing thought di-vine....... Wealth su-

per-nal, Life e-ter-nal All the Fa-ther has is mine.

168 We are workers all

FRANCIS J. GABLE

EDNA GIESELMAN

Tempo di marcia.

1. We're work-ers all at U - ni - ty school, We love to laugh and to grow;
2. The work we do at U - ni - ty school Means joy and peace to all;

We live to learn, we learn to live, To spread the truth we know.
We think the thot, we speak the word, And God heeds ev - 'ry call.

CHORUS.

U - N - I - T - Y, U - NI - TY, ... We've found the Truth that

makes us FREE; .... We send you a mes - sage of

Truth, light, and love, We're hap - py folks at U - NI - TY.........

169   Unity

FRANCIS J. GABLE   EDNA GIESELMAN

Tempo di marcia

1. We fol-low Christ the U - ni - ty way, The way of stud-y and prayer,
2. The time we spend in U - ni - ty tho't Brings joy and bless-ing to all,
3. The prayer of faith is U - ni - ty's prayer, To bless, to pros-per, to heal,
4. It's joy to feel the U - ni - ty bond, At one with Fa-ther and Son,
5. We glo - ry in our U - ni - ty growth In bod - y, spir - it, and soul,

When help we need, to Him we turn, And find Him al - ways there.
We think the thought, we speak the word, And God heeds ev - 'ry call.
As we be - lieve, it does its work, His pres - ence to re - veal.
For when we find the Christ with - in, His per - fect work is done.
To see the Christ in ev - 'ry one— That makes us well and whole.

CHORUS

U - N - I - T - Y, U - NI - TY, We love the Truth that makes us free:............ We broad-cast a mes-sage of Truth, light, and love: We live with God in U - ni - ty..............

170   The Joy of Truth

FRANCIS J. GABLE

FRANGKISER

1. Blos - som lift - ing to the light,.......... Bask - ing
2. Sun - shine spreads its joy a - far,.......... Hap - py

in its gla - mour bright;.......... Do you know that you are
shines the dis - tant star,.......... All God's world is filled with

giv - ing   Les - sons sweet in joy of liv - ing,
light - ness   And our hearts re-flect its bright - ness.

Bring - ing close in vi - sion clear.......... Might - y
Blessed by hap - pi - ness and joy,.......... Naught can

source of joy and cheer?.......... Love of God to us you're
sad - den or an - noy,.......... While we read the end - less

The Joy of Truth

171 My Heart Is Pure

ANONYMOUS

CARL MOERZ

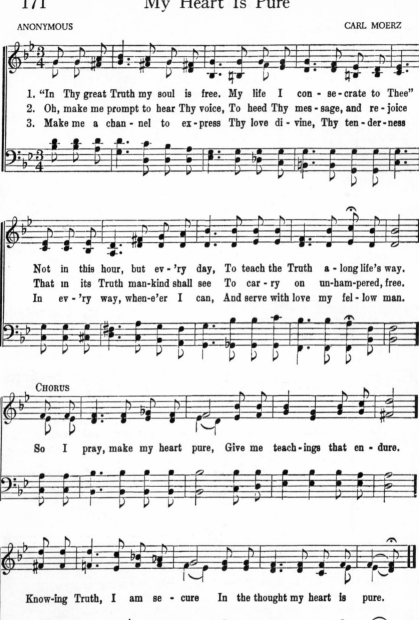

1. "In Thy great Truth my soul is free. My life I con - se - crate to Thee"
2. Oh, make me prompt to hear Thy voice, To heed Thy mes - sage, and re - joice
3. Make me a chan - nel to ex - press Thy love di - vine, Thy ten - der - ness

Not in this hour, but ev - 'ry day, To teach the Truth a - long life's way.
That in its Truth man-kind shall see To car - ry on un-ham-pered, free.
In ev - 'ry way, when-e'er I can, And serve with love my fel - low man.

CHORUS

So I pray, make my heart pure, Give me teach - ings that en - dure.

Know-ing Truth, I am se - cure In the thought my heart is pure.

172 The Path of Truth

FLORENCE R. GUIOTT

FLORENCE R. GUIOTT

1. Gra - cious Sav - ior, keep me safe - ly by Thy side,
2. All a - long the path - way Thy thought flow - ers grow,
3. Thanks be to our Fa - ther for His gift di - vine,

And should dan - ger threat - en, there may I a - bide.
Fill my heart with glad - ness, for I love them so.
For His lov - ing care for those of ev - 'ry clime.

I could nev - er wan - der far a - way from Thee,
As the way leads high - er, oft seems rough and steep,
While we learn the pur - pose of the per - fect way,

Since the path of Truth has now been re - vealed to me.
Then the dove of Truth o'er me will love's vig - il keep.
Praise Him for the path that leads to a bright - er day.

173 Since God Is All in All

F. B. WHITNEY

FRANGKISER

1. Since God is all in all to me There is no hate or fear,
2. Since God is all in all to me There is no lack of health,
3. Since God is all in all to me There is no time, no past,

For love is all there is to see And God as love is near.
For He sup-plies my life with good, Is man-i-fest as wealth.
No vain re-gret for days gone by, No joy that did not last.

If God is real-ly all I know, And all that fills my life
If God is real-ly all I know, I give no thought to sin;
If God is real-ly all I know, With Him I'm sat-is-fied,

In Truth, there is no e-vil thing—No pain, no fear, no strife.
No im-pure tho't, un-ho-ly deed, Can touch the Christ with-in.
And in His love I rest se-cure, And in His peace a-bide.

The Blessed Way

IRENE STANLEY

CARL MOERZ

1. "Come, walk with Me the bless - ed way," I heard the Christ in-
2. "I am the way, the truth, the life, Whence men of meek - ness,
3. "The bless - ed way! Here God im - parts The vi - sion to un-

dwell - ing say, "The way of love, the way of peace, Of
not of strife, In - her - it earth and sea and air As
sul - lied hearts. This way your soul was meant to go To

joy that pass - ing days in - crease; Where hun - gry, thirst - ing
God has made them, whole and fair. Here men show mer - cy,
find the king - dom here be - low. Come, walk with Me this

souls are fed, And mourn - ers glad - dened, com - fort - ed.
and ob - tain In time of drought the sav - ing rain.
bless - ed way," I heard the Christ in - dwell - ing say.

Awake, Awake

CARRIE WARD LYON   CARRIE WARD LYON

Joyously

1. A - wake, a - wake, the night is past, Let morn-ing dawn in ev - 'ry heart;
2. The breath of heav'n is on the hills, A sap-phire glow is on the sea,
3. The fu-ture waits for men of sight, World build-ers, men that dare and do,

No more is heard the thun - der blast, The clouds of war and dark-ness part.
All na - ture with sweet won - der thrills With rap - ture of ex - pect - an - cy,
To car - ry on the torch of right, And make their no-blest dreams come true.

A - wake, a - wake, for - get your pain, And sing the song of life a - gain.
As though its Lord a bless - ing gave To field and flow'r, to cloud and wave,
Build, build a - gain! The an-cient wrong Crum-bles be - fore your might - y song.

The flute of peace in morn - ing mood Is call - ing us to broth - er - hood.
And to the spir - it that can be At peace with all hu - man - i - ty.
Build on war's ruins, O val - iant youth, Build well, in Spir - it and in Truth.

176 My Spirit Yearns

FRANCIS J. GABLE

FRANGKISER

1. My spir-it yearns to be one with Him Who is life and joy and health;
2. In u - ni - ty is the breath of life, That ex - alts the soul of man;
3. When Spir-it speaks I will heed the words Of its gen - tle voice with-in;

I long to dwell in the pres-ence sweet Of the source of all my wealth.
In har - mo - ny I may find a part In the Fa-ther's lov-ing plan.
I keep my steps in the path it shows Till the vic - to - ry I win.

CHORUS

I would know the way of lib-er-ty, Hu-mil-i-ty, true u-ni-ty;

I would seek the path e-ter-nal-ly Of u-ni-ty with God.

177 My Heart Is Smiling Smiles To-day

F. B. WHITNEY

HENRIETTA DIPPMAN GRISWOLD

Cheerfully

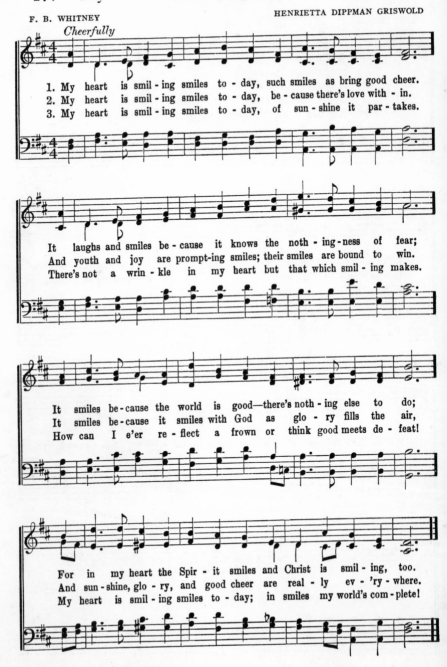

1. My heart is smil - ing smiles to - day, such smiles as bring good cheer.
2. My heart is smil - ing smiles to - day, be - cause there's love with - in.
3. My heart is smil - ing smiles to - day, of sun - shine it par - takes.

It laughs and smiles be - cause it knows the noth - ing - ness of fear;
And youth and joy are prompt-ing smiles; their smiles are bound to win.
There's not a wrin - kle in my heart but that which smil - ing makes.

It smiles be - cause the world is good—there's noth - ing else to do;
It smiles be - cause it smiles with God as glo - ry fills the air,
How can I e'er re - flect a frown or think good meets de - feat!

For in my heart the Spir - it smiles and Christ is smil - ing, too.
And sun - shine, glo - ry, and good cheer are real - ly ev - 'ry - where.
My heart is smil - ing smiles to - day; in smiles my world's com - plete!

Freedom Calls

E. C. HERZOG

E. C. HERZOG

1. Hear the call the trump-et sounds; It's call-ing you, it's
2. Hear the cho-rus that re-plies! A might-y host is

call-ing me. O'er the land the call re-sounds, It's bid-ding us be
an-swer-ing. Fac-es lift-ed to the skies, Oh, heed the song they

free. "All your cares you may dis-pel, As you live the free-ing
sing! "For-ward in the Truth we go, And we want all men to

Truth; And for-ev-er you may dwell In ra-di-ant youth."
see That when they the Truth shall know, They too may be free."

How Other Could It Be

GEO. BLAKESLEY LITTLE   GEO. BLAKESLEY LITTLE

Andante

1. What love's own heart hath planned Life plac - es in my hand,
2. And though my eyes be blind, And dark - ness cloud my mind,
3. Though fears and pains af - fright And foes a - rise in might,

God's love and life in - fold - ing me; How oth - er could it be!
God's love and life are guid - ing me. How oth - er could it be!
God's love and life are guard - ing me. How oth - er could it be!

With - in my heart more clear I sense a pres - ence dear,
And thus with - in, with - out, The one life all a - bout,
And so my voice I raise In joy, in trust, in praise

God's love and life un - fold in me; How oth - er could it be!
God's love and life are mold - ing me; How oth - er could it be!
To Him who all things is to me. How oth - er could it be!

180 Resurgence

ERNEST C. WILSON

FRANGKISER

1. To make mistakes if needs I must, And yet from out their mold'ring dust Remold their
2. To rise from death of dreams, nor rue Their shattered fragments; build a-new A great-er

forms of clay, and trust God's breath to viv - i - fy their earth:
dream and make it true— Thus shall the soul be born a - gain!

181 Awaken

LIDA R. HARDY

LEW HATTON

1. O sons of the new age, a - wak - en! Your tri-umph at last is at hand.
2. Leave off pet - ty likes and am - bi - tions; Then stir up the gift that's with - in,
3. The great goal is not in the dis - tance, It's nei - ther a - far nor be - yond;

A - wake from your dull-ness and stu - por And fol - low the Master's com - mand.
Thro' serv - ice and love for the breth - ren, That all the great son-ship may win.
'Tis here, and the note has been sound - ed! How man - y true souls will re - spond?

CHORUS

A - wak - en, a - wak - en, And fol - low the Mas - ter's com - mand.

Forgive! Forget!

F. B. WHITNEY

FRANGKISER

1. That slight mis-deed of yes-ter-day, why should it mar to-day?
2. For-give your-self for thought-less-ness. Do not con-demn the past;
3. You'll al-ways have a Friend at hand, who will for-give, for-get;

The thing he said, the thing you did has long since passed a - way.
For it is gone with its mis-takes, its mem-'ry can-not last.
Who sees you not as one who erred, who's loy - al to you yet,

For yes - ter - day was but a trial; to - day you will suc - ceed,
For - get the fail - ures and mis-deeds that from ex - pe - rience rise.
Be - holds in you no e - vil thought or e - ven trace of sin.

And from mis-takes of yes - ter - day will come some no - ble deed.
Why should you let your head be bowed? Lift up your heart and eyes.
In you He sees the one He loves, the one who's bound to win.

183 Where the Shepherd leads I'll go

A. P. COBB, Alt.

J. H. FILLMORE

1. Thru the mead-ows green, in - vit - ing, Where the Shep-herd leads I'll go;
2. O'er the mount-ain high and ho - ly, Where the Shep-herd leads I'll go;
3. All His love and mer - cy heed - ing, Where the Shep-herd leads I'll go;

Thru the gloom, His pres - ence light - ing, Where the Shep-herd leads I'll go.
Thru the val - ley, peace-ful, low - ly, Where the Shep-herd leads I'll go.
On the home-ward way He's lead - ing, Where the Shep-herd leads I'll go.

CHORUS.

Thru the morn - ing's ro - sy gleam - ing, Thru the noon of

splen - dor beam - ing, Thru the twi - light shad - ows stream - ing,

rit.

Where the Shepherd leads I'll go, I'll go, Where the Shepherd leads I'll go.

184 What About Today?

ANONYMOUS

MARGARET RIGBY

1. We shall do so much in the years to come, But what have we
2. We shall be so kind in the aft - er - while; But what have we

done to - day? We shall give our gold in a prince - ly sum;
been to - day? We shall bring to each lone - ly life a smile;

But what did we give to - day? We shall lift the heart and
But what have we brought to - day? We shall give to Truth a

dry the tear, We shall plant a hope in the place of fear, We shall
grand - er birth And to stead - fast faith a deep - er worth. We shall

speak the words of love and cheer; But what did we speak to - day?
feed the hun - ger - ing souls of earth; But whom have we fed to - day?

185 He's Standing by Me All the While

F. B. WHITNEY

FRANGKISER

1. He's stand-ing by me all the while; He'd have me look to Him and smile,
2. He's stand-ing by me all the time, It mat-ters not the hour or clime.
3. He's stand-ing by me night and day. I some-times think I hear Him say;

To look a - way from doubt and fear And know that He is stand-ing near.
I can - not fal - ter, can - not fail, His love for - ev - er will pre - vail.
"Just lean on Me and have no fear And some good bless - ing will ap - pear;

And some-times when the shad-ows fall, I need to know that God is all;
I'll not com-plain, my lot be - moan, I'll ne'er a - gain think I'm a - lone;
Just lift your thought to Me and know That naught but Truth can e'er be so."

But need no lon - ger be a - fraid, For Je - sus is at hand to aid.
For Je - sus stands at hand to cheer And have me know He's ver - y near.
I al - ways feel that I can try When I know Je - sus is near by.

186 Out of Shadows into Light

A. O. AUSTIN

CARL MOERZ

1. Hand in hand now walk with Je - sus, Christ will cast your fears a - way;
2. Let your heart, with love re - joic - ing, Cast all sin and sor - row out.

From the dark of er - ror's shad - ow Walk in - to the light of day.
Lov - ing Christ, your on - ly Sav - ior, You shall know no fear or doubt.

Like the bright warm rays of sun - shine, Love of Christ, who leads the way,
With your hand in His He'll guide you; In His path you'll find the way.

Turns all dark - ness in - to sun - light. For, in Spir - it, Truth's the way.
Turn from er - ror and from dark - ness, Let your light shine forth to - day.

187 Oneness with God

ELIZABETH J. MOYER

GEO. MARKS EVANS

1. One with Him whose match-less pow - er Guides His worlds thro' bound-less space;
2. Be ye per - fect as the Fa - ther, With Christ's life your life im - bue;

One with Him whose love un - meas - ured Kin - dles hope in ev - 'ry race,
"Bide with me," so saith the Mas - ter, "That My words may live in you,

Kin - dles hope in ev - 'ry race. One with Thee, O gra - cious
That My words may live in you." In this realm of Truth and

Fa - ther, One with Christ, Thine own dear Son; One in thought and as - pi -
Spir - it, Wis-dom, pow - er, love un - told Mold our thoughts and guide our

ra - tion. On - ly thus Thy will is done. On - ly thus Thy will is done.
foot-steps. Peace and joy our lives in - fold. Peace and joy our lives in - fold.

188   Still, Still with Thee

H. B. STOWE   Arr. from MENDELSSOHN

1. Still, still with Thee, when pur - ple morn - ing break - eth, When the bird
2. A - lone with Thee a - mid the mys - tic shad - ows, The sol - emn
3. So shall it be at last in that bright morn - ing When the soul
4. I can - not lose Thee. Still in Thee a - bid - ing, The end is

wak - eth and the shad - ows flee; Fair - er than morn - ing, love - lier
hush of Na - ture new - ly born; A - lone with Thee, in breath-less
wak - eth and the shad - ows flee; Oh, in that hour, fair - er than
clear, how wide so - e'er I roam; The law that holds the worlds my

than the day - light Dawns the sweet con - scious-ness, I am with Thee.
ad - o - ra - tion, In the calm dew and fresh-ness of the morn.
day - light dawn - ing, Shall rise the glo - rious thought, I am with Thee.
steps is guid - ing, And I must rest at last in Thee, my home.

189   From All that Dwell below the Skies

ISAAC WATTS and WESLEY   JOHN HATTON

1. From all that dwell be - low the skies, Let the Cre - a - tor's praise a - rise;
2. E - ter - nal are Thy mer - cies, Lord; E - ter - nal truth at - tends Thy word;
3. In ev - 'ry land be - gin the song; To ev - 'ry land the strains be - long;

From All that Dwell below the Skies

Let the Re-deem-er's name be sung, Thro' ev-'ry land, by ev-'ry tongue.
Thy praise shall sound from shore to shore, Till suns shall rise and set no more.
In cheer-ful sounds all voic - es raise, And fill the world with loud-est praise.

190   Omnipresence

PSALMS 139: 7-10

C. H. S.

CLARA H. SCOTT

1. Al-ways with me! I can nev - er Stray be - yond His ten - der care,
2. Al-ways with me! Love so ten - der Feels each trem-bling breath of prayer,
3. Al-ways with me! In His treas-ures, Free, a - bun - dant, I may share,
4. Al-ways with me! Ev - 'ry bur - den His strong arm will help me bear,

For our God is om - ni - pres - ent, Here and there and ev - 'ry-where,
For our God is ev - er lis - t'ning, And His love is ev - 'ry-where,
For He holds them ev - er read - y For His chil - dren ev - 'ry-where,
For our God is om - ni - pres - ent, With His chil - dren ev - 'ry-where,

m   *p*   *slow*   *m*   *tempo*

Yes, ev - 'ry-where, and ev - 'ry-where, Here and there and ev - 'ry-where.
Yes, ev - 'ry-where, and ev - 'ry-where, And His love is ev - 'ry-where.
Yes, ev - 'ry-where, and ev - 'ry-where, For His chil - dren ev - 'ry-where.
Yes, ev - 'ry-where, and ev - 'ry-where, With His chil - dren ev - 'ry-where.

191   A Rendezvous with Youth

WILMET L. CUMMINGS   GEO. MARKS EVANS

1. I have a ren-dez-vous with youth...... My soul is ev - er
2. I see no e - vil with my eyes;...... No e - vil thoughts as-
3. And so with all the chang-ing years...... My own shall come to

young. I hear no e - vil with my ears,...... Or
sail. I have a ren - dez - vous with youth,..... And
me. I have a ren - dez - vous with youth...... The

voice it with my tongue,.. Or voice it with my
love and joy pre - vail,..... And love and joy pre-
best is yet to be,...... The best is yet to

tongue,..... Or voice it with my tongue.......
vail,........ And love and joy pre - vail.........
be,........ The best is yet to be...........

How Silently, How Silently

LEORA CARLSON   LEORA CARLSON

DUET

1. You ask me how Christ comes to me, My heart His pres-ence fills?
2. A tryst-ing place with Him a-lone: There is no place so fair;
3. A-part with Him, a-lone with Him, There flows in-to my heart

He comes as si-lent-ly as the dawn Comes o-ver the wak-ened hills.
And per-fume of the flow'rs of heav'n Is borne up-on the air.
A sweet re-pose, a gen-tle-ness That earth can-not im-part.

CHORUS

How si-lent-ly, how si-lent-ly Christ makes His pres-ence known!

'Tis on-ly when the soul is hushed He comes un-to His own.

193 Blessed Assurance

FANNY J. CROSBY

MRS. J. F. KNAPP

1. Bless - ed as - sur - ance, Je - sus is mine! Oh, what a fore - taste of
2. Per - fect sub - mis - sion, per - fect de - light, Vi - sions of rap - ture now
3. Per - fect sub - mis - sion, all is at rest, I in my Sav - ior am

glo - ry di - vine! Heir of sal - va - tion, pur - chase of God,
burst on my sight; An - gels de - scend - ing, bring from a - bove,
hap - py and blest; Watch-ing and wait - ing, look-ing a - bove,

CHORUS

Born of His Spir - it, washed in His blood.
Ech - oes of mer - cy, whis-pers of love. This is my sto - ry, this is my
Filled with His good - ness, lost in His love.

song, Prais-ing my Sav - ior all the day long; This is my sto - ry,

this is my song, Prais-ing my Sav - ior all the day long.

The Secret Place

FRANCIS J. GABLE

FRANGKISER

1. I know a gar-den bright and fair, Where I draw near to God in prayer;
2. I meet the Fa-ther face to face On-ly with-in the se-cret place,

There with a smile He meets me, Warm-ly in love He greets me.
And there in sweet com-mun - ion With all His love find un - ion.

CHORUS

In the beau-ti-ful gar-den of love .... Where the Spir-it de-scends as a dove, ... I would lin-ger in prayer, For His pres-ence is there In the beau-ti-ful gar-den of love. ....

I Will

WORDS SELECTED

ROGER VALLANZ

1. I will start a-new this morn-ing With a high-er, fair-er creed;
2. I will look some-times a-bout me For the things that mer-it praise;
3. I will not be swayed by en-vy When my ri-val's strength is shown;

I will cease to stand com-plain-ing Of my ruth-less neigh-bor's greed;
I will search for hid-den beau-ties That e-lude the grum-bler's gaze.
I will not de-ny his mer-it, But I'll strive to prove my own.

I will cease to sit re-pin-ing While my du-ty's call is clear,
I will try to find con-tent-ment In the paths that I must tread;
I will try to see the beau-ty Spread be-fore me, rain or shine;

I will waste no more time whin-ing, And my heart shall know no fear.
I will cease to have re-sent-ment When an-oth-er moves a-head.
I will cease to preach your du-ty And be more con-cerned with mine.

196   A Prayer

JULIANNE S. OTT

GEO. MARKS EVANS

1. God, let me laugh with those who laugh, And hap - ly lend a tone......
2. And let me play with those who play, Re - veal - ing thus the truth......
3. Lord, let me pray with those who pray With heav - y heart or light,......

Of joy - ous faith to mer - ri - ment Less hope - ful than my own........
That God planned play-time as the key To life's e - ter - nal youth.......
And grant that through me Thou shalt show Them how to pray a - right........

Oh, let me sing with those who sing, And teach them thus Thy song.....
And let me work with those who work, To show, what - e'er their task,....
But let me wak - en those who sleep With some word Thou shalt give.....

Of love and peace and hap - pi - ness, To thrill them all day long.....
'Tis God's own work, and gains for them The bless - ings that they ask......
That speaks of Heav'n as here and now And bids them rise and live!.....

197 Glory to God!

MARY O. PAGE

CLARA H. SCOTT

1. Glo-ry to God! hal-le-lu-jahs we raise, Songs of re-joic-ing we
2. Glo-ry to God! hal-le-lu-jahs a-gain! Pow'r from yon heav-en He
3. Glo-ry to God! hal-le-lu-jahs we give, Hon-or the Fa-ther who

ut-ter with praise; God in His good-ness who seek-eth to bless,
giv-eth to men; Heir with His Christ ev-'ry mis-sion to bear,
taught us to live; One with Je-ho-vah, His love we pro-claim,

Crowns us with mer-cy and right-eous-ness. Glo-ry to God! be the
We with His con-quests for-ev-er may share. Glo-ry to God! be the
Let all our la-bors be sealed with His name. Glo-ry to God! be the

REFRAIN

f

end-less re-frain; Glo-ry to God! sing it o-ver a-gain! God in His
end-less re-frain; Glo-ry to God! sing it o-ver a-gain! Heir with His
end-less re-frain; Glo-ry to God! sing it o-ver a-gain! One with Je-

Glory to God!

good-ness who seek-eth to bless, Crowns us with mer-cy and right-eous-ness.
Christ ev-'ry mis-sion to bear, We in His con-quests for-ev-er may share.
ho - vah, His love we pro-claim, Let all our la-bors be sealed with His name.

198   With a Perfect Heart

HELEN L. MANNING   COL. 1: 28   WARD ROCKWELL

Joyfully

1. Per - fect is my heart be - fore Thee, Per - fect walk I in Thy ways;
2. Per - fect free - dom! I de - clare it! For the Truth has made me free.

Per - fect love e'en now re - stores me, Per - fect is my song of praise.
Per - fect peace! yea, naught shall mar it, For my mind is stayed on Thee.

REFRAIN

I will walk with a per - fect heart, Love has cast out fear;

I will walk with a per - fect heart, Joy has dried each tear.

Fairest Lord Jesus

CRUSADER'S HYMN

ANONYMOUS

Arr. by RICHARD S. WILLIS

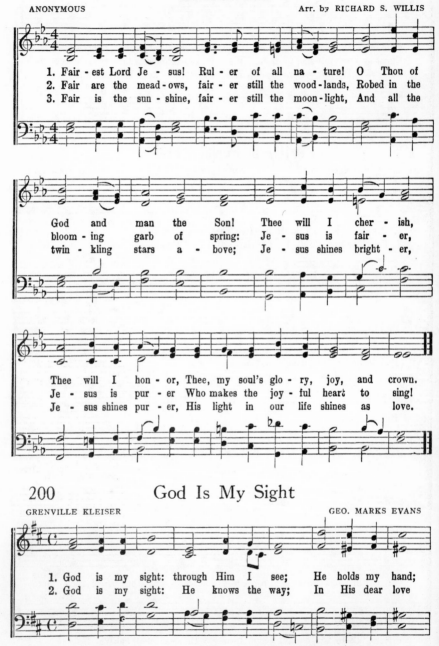

1. Fair - est Lord Je - sus! Rul - er of all na - ture! O Thou of
2. Fair are the mead - ows, fair - er still the wood - lands, Robed in the
3. Fair is the sun - shine, fair - er still the moon - light, And all the

God and man the Son! Thee will I cher - ish,
bloom - ing garb of spring: Je - sus is fair - er,
twin - kling stars a - bove; Je - sus shines bright - er,

Thee will I hon - or, Thee, my soul's glo - ry, joy, and crown.
Je - sus is pur - er Who makes the joy - ful heart to sing!
Je - sus shines pur - er, His light in our life shines as love.

200

God Is My Sight

GRENVILLE KLEISER

GEO. MARKS EVANS

1. God is my sight: through Him I see; He holds my hand;
2. God is my sight: He knows the way; In His dear love

God Is My Sight

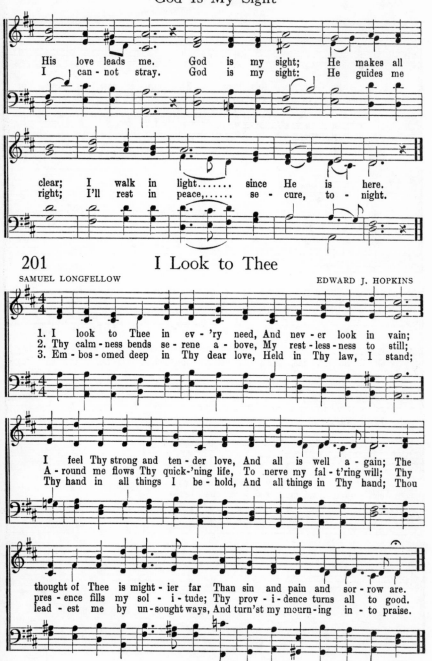

His love leads me. God is my sight; He makes all
I can-not stray. God is my sight: He guides me

clear; I'll walk in light...... since He is here.
right; I'll rest in peace,...... se - cure, to - night.

201 I Look to Thee

SAMUEL LONGFELLOW

EDWARD J. HOPKINS

1. I look to Thee in ev-'ry need, And nev-er look in vain;
2. Thy calm-ness bends se-rene a-bove, My rest-less-ness to still;
3. Em-bos-omed deep in Thy dear love, Held in Thy law, I stand;

I feel Thy strong and ten-der love, And all is well a-gain; The
A-round me flows Thy quick-'ning life, To nerve my fal-t'ring will; Thy
Thy hand in all things I be-hold, And all things in Thy hand; Thou

thought of Thee is might-ier far Than sin and pain and sor-row are.
pres-ence fills my sol-i-tude; Thy prov-i-dence turns all to good.
lead-est me by un-sought ways, And turn'st my mourn-ing in-to praise.

202 Prayer

REBECCA BUDROW

MANUELA BUDROW

1. O Fa - ther, in this hour To - geth - er now we pray For
2. Give strength to those who fal - ter Be - neath their heav - y cross. Lead

all Thy need - y chil - dren Who want Thy help to - day; One prayer, one
forth all those who wan - der Up - on this earth at loss. Oh, com - fort

voice, one an - them U - nit - ed to Thee raise. O Fa - ther, in Thy
all who suf - fer, With hope their sor - rows ease; O Lord, to all Thy

CHORUS

mer - cy Turn not Thy lov - ing face.
chil - dren Send light, and love, and peace. Fa - ther, Fa - ther, at-

tend with love our prayer, Fa - ther, Fa - ther, oh, keep us in Thy care.

203 Thy Will Be Done

WINNIE L. JENKS

GEO. MARKS EVANS

1. In old - en.... time...... I bowed my head In
2. The blow fell... not....... In glad sur - prise I
3. Thy will it.... is........ that we should be From

re - sig - na - tion deep and said, ... "Thy will be
raised to Thee my tear - dimmed eyes—... "Thy will be
er - ror's sub - tle ways set free;.... "Thy will be

done," Then wait - ed for...... the blow to fall...... That
done." And then I learned,.. O God most high!.... Thy
done." Sin, sick - ness, er - ror, all must fall,..... For

took from me my world - ly all, "Thy will be done."
will can bring but bless - ings nigh; "Thy will be done."
Thou art here and Thou art all; "Thy will be done."

Myself His Very Nest

VIVIAN YEISER LARAMORE   CARLETON A. SCHEINERT

1. God whis - pers in the for - est, He breathes in blades of grass;
2. But clos - er still I find Him, My - self His ver - y nest,

All day be - fore my door - step In friends I see Him pass;
When deep in med - i - ta - tion I lay me down to rest

The rose that climbs the trel - lis, The bird that combs the sky,
In that sweet un - der - stand - ing Of God and man as one

And lit - tle rain - drops danc - ing Tell me that God is nigh.
Then does the Fa - ther's boun - ty Make beau - ti - ful the son!

205   Come Ye Apart Awhile

B. T. JAMESON

Adapted from J. S. BACH

1. Come ye a-part a - while In - to the mount and rest,
2. Be - hold, the Christ is here His wis - dom to im - part,
3. Come ye a-part a - while, Thine ev - 'ry need con - fess

In - to that high and ho - ly place That God Him - self hath blessed.
The con - trite spir - it to re - vive, Re - store the hum - ble heart.
Un - to the One sent forth from God To com - fort, heal, and bless.

206   Holy Spirit, Truth Divine

M. E. COLES

An Invocation

J. P. WHITE

1. Ho - ly Spir - it, Truth di - vine, Dawn up - on this soul of mine;
2. Ho - ly Spir - it, love di - vine, Glow with - in this heart of mine;
3. Ho - ly Spir - it, pow'r di - vine, Fill and nerve this will of mine;

Word of God and in - ward light, Wake my spir - it, clear my sight.
Kin - dle ev - 'ry high de - sire, Burn up self in Thy pure fire.
Be my law, and I shall be Firm - ly bound, yet ev - er free.

Heaven Is Here

THEODOSIA SMITH

FRANCIS J. HAYDN

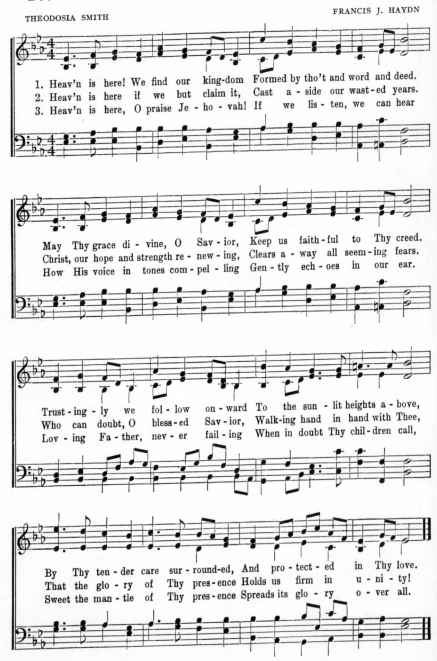

1. Heav'n is here! We find our king-dom Formed by tho't and word and deed.
2. Heav'n is here if we but claim it, Cast a - side our wast - ed years.
3. Heav'n is here, O praise Je - ho - vah! If we lis - ten, we can hear

May Thy grace di - vine, O Sav - ior, Keep us faith - ful to Thy creed.
Christ, our hope and strength re - new - ing, Clears a - way all seem - ing fears.
How His voice in tones com - pel - ling Gen - tly ech - oes in our ear.

Trust - ing - ly we fol - low on - ward To the sun - lit heights a - bove,
Who can doubt, O bless - ed Sav - ior, Walk - ing hand in hand with Thee,
Lov - ing Fa - ther, nev - er fail - ing When in doubt Thy chil - dren call,

By Thy ten - der care sur - round - ed, And pro - tect - ed in Thy love.
That the glo - ry of Thy pres - ence Holds us firm in u - ni - ty!
Sweet the man - tle of Thy pres - ence Spreads its glo - ry o - ver all.

208 I Love to Tell the Story

KATHERINE HANKEY

WILLIAM G. FISCHER

1. I love to tell the sto-ry Of un-seen things a-bove, Of Je-sus and His glo-ry, Of Je-sus and His love, I love to tell the sto-ry, Be-cause I know 'tis true, It sat-is-fies my longings, As noth-ing else can do.

2. I love to tell the sto-ry; More won-der-ful it seems Than all the gold-en fan-cies Of all our gold-en dreams. I love to tell the sto-ry, It did so much for me; And that is just the rea-son I tell it now to thee.

3. I love to tell the sto-ry; 'Tis pleas-ant to re-peat What seems each time I tell it More won-der-ful-ly sweet. I love to tell the sto-ry, For some have nev-er heard The mes-sage of sal-va-tion From God's own Holy Word.

4. I love to tell the sto-ry; For those who know it best Seem hun-ger-ing and thirst-ing To hear it like the rest. And when in scenes of glo-ry I sing the new, new song, 'Twill be the old, old sto-ry, That I have loved so long.

CHORUS

I love to tell the sto-ry! 'Twill be my theme in glo-ry To tell the old, old sto-ry Of Je-sus and His love.

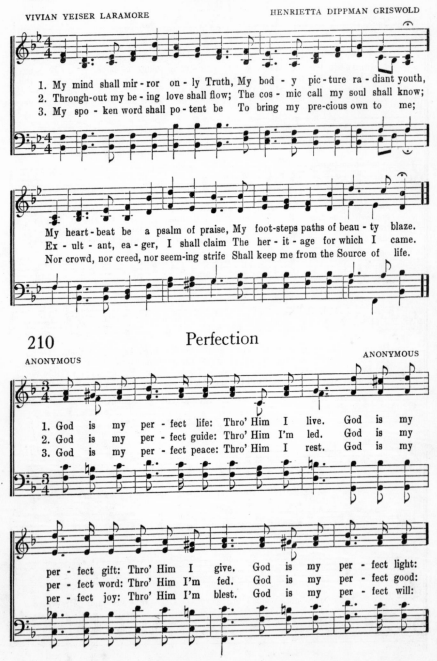

209

Affirmation

VIVIAN YEISER LARAMORE

HENRIETTA DIPPMAN GRISWOLD

1. My mind shall mir-ror on-ly Truth, My bod-y pic-ture ra-diant youth,
2. Through-out my be-ing love shall flow; The cos-mic call my soul shall know;
3. My spo-ken word shall po-tent be To bring my pre-cious own to me;

My heart-beat be a psalm of praise, My foot-steps paths of beau-ty blaze.
Ex-ult-ant, ea-ger, I shall claim The her-it-age for which I came.
Nor crowd, nor creed, nor seem-ing strife Shall keep me from the Source of life.

210

Perfection

ANONYMOUS

ANONYMOUS

1. God is my per-fect life: Thro' Him I live. God is my
2. God is my per-fect guide: Thro' Him I'm led. God is my
3. God is my per-fect peace: Thro' Him I rest. God is my

per-fect gift: Thro' Him I give. God is my per-fect light:
per-fect word: Thro' Him I'm fed. God is my per-fect good:
per-fect joy: Thro' Him I'm blest. God is my per-fect will:

Perfection

Thro' Him I see. God is my per-fect voice: He speaks thro' me.
My way is clear. God is my per-fect love, And He is here.
Thro' me 'tis done. God is my per-fect all, And we are one.

211 Praise God

FANNIE HERRON WINGATE

W. C. JORDAN

1. If you would start the day a-right, Praise God, praise God.
2. No mat-ter what there seems to be, Praise God, praise God.

If you'd be glad from morn till night, Praise God. If
Tho' you must cross some dread Red Sea, Praise God. You

sun-shine bright-ens all your day Or clouds loom dark a-cross your way,
soon will see the rain-bow's hue, For by His hand He'll lead you thro',

Yet al-ways, as you sing or pray, Praise God.
And glo-rious-ly de-liv-er you— Praise God!

212   Lord, I Yield to Thee

FRANCIS J. GABLE   FRANGKISER

1. There's a veil of dark - ness lift - ing, Sin and shad - ows
2. Truth will lift me, Truth will free me If I o - pen

dis - ap - pear. 'Tis the dawn of Truth ap - proach - ing; Feel its
wide my heart. Let its sooth - ing pres - ence heal me, Let it

CHORUS

cleans - ing pres - ence near........ The life stream of God now
fill its per - fect part........

flows through me; It quick - ens, it strength - ens, it makes me free. No

pow - er so cleans-ing can ev - er be. Lord, I yield to Thee.

213 Song of Faith

B. Y. WILLIAMS

ALICE MORSE GLOVER

1. I shall not fear: The ter-rors that con-found me Van-ish at length, like mists be-fore the sun. Know-ing His arm is ev-er-more a-round me, What need I fear, what per-ils need I shun!

2. I shall not want: How could that tho't as-sail me, Know-ing His wealth is in-fi-nite in-deed! How could I think His love would ev-er fail me, Or dream His boun-ty would not meet my need!

CHORUS

I shall not fail, Nor shall my task ap-pall me, Tho' it may seem too heav-y for my hands; I know that He who to the task did call me Will give me strength to meet the task's de-mands.

The Faith to Pray

VIVIAN YEISER LARAMORE

MILTON MARQUOTE

1. It mat-ters not how far we stray, The Fa-ther's arms are
2. We on-ly need to trust Him more And place our hand in

there; We on-ly need the faith to pray For His un-ceas-ing
His, If we would find the o-pen door And know where heav-en

care. We on-ly need to call His name A-bove the clos-ing
is. It mat-ters not how steep the way! Since His dear love em-

night To catch a-gain the in-ner flame That leads to ways of light.
pow'rs, We on-ly need the faith to pray, And lo, the goal is ours.

215   My Faith Looks Up to Thee

THEODOSIA SMITH

LOWELL MASON

1. My faith looks up to Thee, Thou Lamb of Cal-va-ry,
2. May Thy rich grace bring joy, All fear and doubt de-stroy,
3. While life's steep path I tread, If mists a-round me spread,

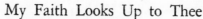

Sav - ior di - vine; O hear me when I pray, Lead me a-
My zeal in - spire; As Thou sus - tain - est me, O may my
With me a - bide; Faith shall my watch-word be, Health and pros-

long Thy way, And let me from this day Be whol - ly Thine.
love for Thee Pure, warm, and change - less be; A liv - ing fire.
per - i - ty, My pre - cious gifts from Thee, Thou art my guide.

216 Trusting and Resting

WRIGHT FIELD   GEO. MARKS EVANS

1. Mine not to wea - ry with thank-less pain, Fig - ur - ing la - bor and loss and gain.
2. Mine not to ques - tion the why and how; Mine but to know that He feeds me now,
3. Mine but to give my best and know Back to my heart the best will flow;
4. Mine not to en - vy an - oth - er's good, Nor to de - prive him if I could;
5. Mine not to struggle—oh, ease - ful tho't! Mine but to know, since I am taught,

Trust-ing and rest-ing, I shall be Clothed in the gar - ments meant for me.
Trust-ing and rest-ing, I shall be Fed with the food that is best for me!
Trust-ing and rest-ing, I shall be En - cir-cled by love, e - ter - nal - ly!
Trust-ing and rest-ing, I can be Sure that my own will come to me!
Trust-ing and rest-ing, I shall be Cared for in life and e - ter - ni - ty!

A Vision

ANNA L. DERSCHELL

CARL MOERZ

1. In mo-ments rare there comes to me A vi-sion un-ex-pect-ed;
2. No mat-ter what life's fu-ture hours May hold of earth-born sad-ness,

I clear-ly see with-in my soul The u-ni-verse re-flect-ed.
I know there comes to me in Truth A her-it-age of glad-ness

I am a part of all that's good, I feel, I know no lim-it,
That far tran-scends all gross-er things—I've caught the vi-sion glo-rious:

The God-in-all stands forth so clear, No fan-cied ills can dim it.
We are a part of all that's good, And good shall be vic-to-rious.

218　Everlasting Love

HELEN L. MANNING

CLARA H. SCOTT

1. Ev - er - last - ing love in - folds me, Om - ni - pres - ent, change-less, true;
2. Shad - ows flee be-fore faiths's brightness, Hope springs up with buoy - ant tread;

Sat - is - fi - eth all my long-ings, Makes me both to will and do.
Health and strength are my com - pan - ions, No more weak-ness, pain, or dread.

I am here the Fa-ther's wit - ness, Might - y words of Truth to speak:
Pow'r comes to me in the si - lence, Fills my soul with rap - ture rare;

Ban - ish er - ror, sin and sick - ness, Lift the bur - dens of the weak.
Faith pro-claims o'er earth's do - min - ion, Wis - dom shines with jew - els fair.

Ev - er - last - ing love in - folds me, Om - ni - pres - ent, changeless, true.
Ev - er - last - ing love in - folds me, Om - ni - pres - ent, changeless, true.

219

Teach Me, O God

BETH HINDS

GEORGE MARKS EVANS

1. Teach me, O God, to cleanse my heart, Make pure my
2. Let my life shine that all may see Thy im - age
3. Not that my soul may gain re - ward, Not that my

mind in ev - 'ry part, And let my ev - 'ry
man - i - fest in me. Let me ex - press through
path may be less hard, But that Thy light may

word ex - press Thy love and joy and ten - der - ness.
ev - 'ry deed The sweet com - pas - sion of Thy creed.
bright - ly shine, To Thee the praise, the glo - ry Thine!

220

My Life Is in Thee

C. H. S.

CLARA H. SCOTT

1. My life is in Thee, Thou om - ni - pres - ent One, My life is in
2. My health is in Thee, Thou om - ni - pres - ent One, My health is in
3. All pow'r is in Thee, Thou om - ni - pres - ent One, All pow'r is in

My Life Is in Thee

Thee, Thou om - ni - pres - ent One. Foun-tain of life Thou art, Spring-ing with-
Thee, Thou om - ni - pres - ent One. All good I draw from Thee, Thy law pre-
Thee, Thou om - ni - pres - ent One. Thus er - ror's chains are riv'n; Heir of the

in each heart; No life from Thee a - part, Thou Good-ness di - vine!
serv - eth me; Help me this truth to see, And prove it di - vine.
wealth of heav'n, To me, His child, is giv'n A free - dom di - vine.

221   I Behold the Christ in You

F. B. WHITNEY

EDNA L. GIESELMAN

1. I be - hold the Christ in you; Here the life of God I see.
2. I be - hold the Christ in you. I can see this as you walk,
3. I be - hold God's love ex-pressed; I can see you filled with pow'r.
4. I be - hold the Christ in you; I can see that per - fect One.

I can see a great peace, too; I can see you whole and free.
I see this in all you do, I can see this as you talk.
I can see you ev - er blessed: See Christ in you hour by hour.
Led by God in all you do, I can see God's work is done.

222 Wonderful Words of Life

P. P. B.

P. P. BLISS

1. Sing them o - ver a - gain to me, Won-der-ful words of life;
2. Christ, the bless - ed One, gives to all, Won-der-ful words of life;
3. Sweet-ly ech - o the gos - pel call, Won-der-ful words of life;

Let me more of their beau - ty see, Won-der-ful words of life;
Sin - ner, list to the lov - ing call, Won-der-ful words of life;
Of - fer par - don and peace to all, Won-der-ful words of life;

Words of life and beau - ty, Teach me faith and du - ty:
All so free - ly giv - en, Woo - ing us to heav - en:
Je - sus, on - ly Sav - ior, Sanc - ti - fy for - ev - er:

REFRAIN

Beau - ti - ful words, won - der - ful words, Won - der - ful words of life;

Beau - ti - ful words, won - der - ful words, Won - der - ful words of life.

223 His Life in Me

FRANCIS J. GABLE

FRANGKISER

1. God's ho - ly pres - ence is in me, His life in me makes me whole.
2. God made my bod - y His tem - ple, Sa - cred and ho - ly and pure;
3. My heart is filled with thanks-giv - ing, Glad - ly to Him I give praise;

His love out-pours, free - ly re - stores Bod - y and mind and soul.
With spir - it filled, glad - ly I build Health that shall long en - dure.
His ten - der care an - swers my prayer, Guides me in all my ways.

CHORUS

His life is in me, From bond - age I'm free, New

foun - tains of health are re - vealed. His breath fills me through, He

gives life a - new, In Him I am blessed and healed.

224 Thou Art My Life

C. H. S.

CLARA H. SCOTT

1. Thou art my life, Thou art my health,........
Thou art my life, Thou art, Thou art my health,
2. Thou art my light, Thou art my pu - ri - ty,
Thou art my light, Thou art, Thou art my puri-ty,
3. Thou art my pow'r, Thou art my might,........
Thou art my pow'r, Thou art, Thou art my might,
4. Thou art my joy, Thou art my peace,........
Thou art my joy, Thou art, Thou art my peace,
5. Thou art my love, Thou art my wis - dom,
Thou art my love, Thou art, Thou art my wis-dom,
6. I am re - newed, I will re - joice,.........
I am re - newed, I will, I will re - joice,

Thou, Lord, hast healed me, Thou, Lord, hast healed me,
Thou, Lord, hast cleansed me, Thou, Lord, hast cleansed me,
Thou, Lord, dost strength-en me, Thou, Lord, dost strength-en me,
Thou, Lord, dost com - fort me, Thou, Lord, dost com - fort me,
Thou, Lord, art guid - ing me, Thou, Lord, art guid - ing me,
Thou, Lord, my glo - ry art, Thou, Lord, my glo - ry art,

Thou, Lord, hast healed me, My trust is in Thee.
Thou, Lord, hast cleansed me, My trust is in Thee.
Thou, Lord, dost strength-en me, My trust is in Thee.
Thou, Lord, dost com - fort me, My trust is in Thee.
Thou, Lord, art guid - ing me, My trust is in Thee.
Thou, Lord, my glo - ry art, My trust is in Thee.

The Grateful Heart

MINOLA MADDY

CARL MOERZ

1. Give me, dear God, a grate-ful heart, A heart to sing and
glow,........ A heart that sees the sun-shine bright, Though
clouds be dark and low......... Give me a grate-ful heart, O
God, That looks to Thee a-bove,........ A heart that
knows no lack or fear When shel-tered in Thy love.

2. My heart has found in Thee con-tent, No need shall ev-er
know........ E-ter-nal life and peace are mine Thy
gra-cious love to show....... And now, dear God, I give my
thanks: In Thee I've found sweet peace,....... In Thee my
joy is made com-plete, Thy love will nev-er cease.

226 Conquering All

THEODOSIA SMITH

NOEL RAY

1. Fol - low the Fa - ther, He'll show you the way; Trust in Him
2. Fol - low the Fa - ther—un - fail - ing His care For us His

al - ways, His word do o - bey. With Truth our watch-word, in
chil - dren! His love all may share. Lis - ten to Spir - it that

faith shall we stand, God's rich - est bless - ings are ours to com - mand.
speaks from with - in; True to His prom - ise, He helps us to win.

CHORUS

Fol - low and trust in Him, True to your dreams with - in.

Truth will the vic - t'ry win, Con - quer - ing all.

Jesus, Lover of My Soul

THEODOSIA SMITH

S. B. MARSH

1. Je - sus, lov - er of my soul, Let Thy strong arms shel - ter me;
2. Hear my praise, most gra-cious One, Let my song to Thee re - sound;
3. Je - sus, lov - er of my soul, Faith re-news, re - stores my sight;

If dark wa - ters near me roll, Lord of all, my ref - uge be.
May Thine ev - er - last - ing grace Al - ways in my life a - bound.
When the voice of Spir - it speaks, Shad - ows van - ish, all is light.

Let me nev - er stray, dear Lord; May my life be made com - plete:
Thou art near; my fears are gone When I fol - low in the Way
Bless-ings flow in - creas - ing - ly, For Thou heed-est ev - 'ry call,

Fill with hope and strength and joy, And with peace make it re - plete.
Lead - ing to the ra-diant heights, And Thy lov - ing call o - bey.
And Thy sweet, pro - tect - ing care Hov-ers gen - tly o - ver all.

228 Man Became a Living Soul

STELLA M. TEMPLEMAN

JEANNETTE H. BRUMBAUGH

1. Some-where down the count-less a - ges Man a liv - ing soul be - came,
2. As one breathes up - on a win - dow, Pris-oned deep in rime and frost,
3. The E - ter - nal in sus-pen - sion Holds the im - age He has made
4. Dares to prove his God - like na - ture, What his soul, and whence it came;
5. Thus a step in ev - o - lu - tion Of the crea-ture tow'rd his Cause

When the breath of the E - ter - nal Touched him with its quick-'ning flame.
And the sol - id in - to va - por Melts, un - seen, yet is not lost;
Of His in - fi - nite per - fec - tion Un - til man, grown un - a - fraid,
While on him the cos - mic Spir - it Breathes a - gain, and yet a - gain.
Shows the des - tined work of god-hood: To re - veal yet high - er laws.

229 Thou Art

VIVIAN YEISER LARAMORE

CARL MOERZ

1. Thou art my strength, O might - y One, In Thee I rest se - cure.
2. Thou art my peace, O pois - ed One. The ev - er - last - ing hills
3. Thou art my wealth, O pre - cious One. With stars Thou crown-est me;
4. Thou art my all, O per - fect One. The hope with - in my heart,

Thou hold - est to my lips the cup Of life di - vine - ly pure;
Pro - claim Thy sweet tran - quil - li - ty, Which gen - tly soothes and stills;
The gold - en sun - light is Thy gift, And ev - 'ry fruit - ful tree;
The song that in the si - lence sings, And all that is, Thou art;

Thou Art

Thou hold-est to my lips the cup Of life di-vine-ly pure.
Pro - claim Thy sweet tran-quil-li - ty, Which gen-tly soothes and stills.
The gold - en sun-light is Thy gift, And ev - 'ry fruit-ful tree.
The song that in the si - lence sings, And all that is, Thou art.

230 The Greater Love

FRANCIS J. GABLE

FRANGKISER

1. O bless - ed day! O glo-rious morn! On which our Lord and Sav - ior rose.
2. A love that has its birth in Christ, In Christ new ris - en from the dead,
3. A love that cheers our wea - ry soul, Dis - pel - ling all our grief and gloom;

Deep, deep with-in our heart is born A great - er love that swells and grows;
And that for a - ges has suf-ficed To up-ward lift each droop-ing head;
While from our heart the e - vil rolls As did the stone from Je - sus' tomb.

CHORUS

Then let the earth with an-thems ring, And let each wea - ry heart be gay,

And all man-kind the ti - dings sing That Christ our Sav - ior rose to - day.

In Heavenly Love Abiding

ANNA L. WARING

DR. S. S. WESLEY

1. In heav'n-ly love a - bid - ing, No change my heart shall fear;
2. Wher - ev - er He may guide me, No want shall turn me back;
3. Green pas - tures are be - fore me, Which yet I have not seen;
And safe is such con - fid - ing, For noth - ing chang - es here.
My Shep - herd is be - side me, And noth - ing can I lack.
Bright skies will soon be o'er me, Where dark - est skies have been.
The storm may roar with - out me, My heart may low be laid,
His wis - dom ev - er wak - eth, His sight is nev - er dim,
My hope I can - not meas - ure, My path to life is free;
But God is round a - bout me, And can I be dis - mayed?
He knows the way He tak - eth, And I will walk with Him.
My Sav - ior has my treas - ure, And He will walk with me.

232   Years Are Coming

ANONYMOUS

FANNIE HERRON WINGATE

1. Years are com - ing, years are go - ing, Creeds may change and pass a - way,
2. Self - ish claims will soon no lon - ger Raise their harsh, dis - cord-ant sounds,

But the pow'r of love is grow - ing Strong-er, sur - er day by day;
For the law of love will con - quer, Burst-ing ha - tred's nar - row bounds;

Be ye as the light of morn - ing, Like the beau-teous dawn un - fold,
Hu - man love will spread a glo - ry Fill - ing men with glad-some mirth,

With your ra - diant lives a - dorn - ing All the world in hues of gold.
Songs of joy pro - claim the sto - ry Of a fair, trans - fig-ured earth.

233 Love Is a Magnet

FRANCIS J. GABLE

FRANGKISER

1. Love is a mag-net that draws to me Rich-es and good with-out end;
2. Love of the Fa-ther a-bides in me, Spread-ing its sweet-ness a-broad,
3. Love in it-self is a price-less gift, Op-u-lence free-ly ex-pressed,

Free-ly and full as a bound-less sea In-to my life they blend.
Draw-ing to me in its cur-rent free All of the wealth of God.
Near-er the Fa-ther the heart to lift, Rich-ly by love I'm blessed.

CHORUS

Lov-ing word, lov-ing deed, Spring-ing from heart di-vine,

Bring to me full-est meed, Mak-ing a-bun-dance mine.

234 New Life

E. HATCH

J. B. DICK

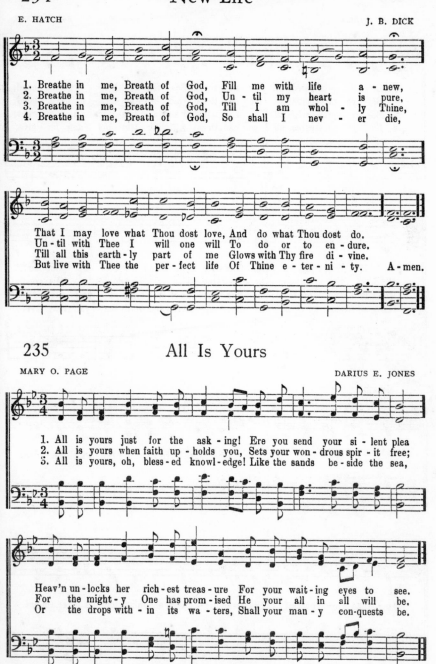

1. Breathe in me, Breath of God, Fill me with life a-new,
2. Breathe in me, Breath of God, Un-til my heart is pure,
3. Breathe in me, Breath of God, Till I am whol-ly Thine,
4. Breathe in me, Breath of God, So shall I nev-er die,

That I may love what Thou dost love, And do what Thou dost do.
Un-til with Thee I will one will To do or to en-dure.
Till all this earth-ly part of me Glows with Thy fire di-vine.
But live with Thee the per-fect life Of Thine e-ter-ni-ty. A-men.

235 All Is Yours

MARY O. PAGE

DARIUS E. JONES

1. All is yours just for the ask-ing! Ere you send your si-lent plea
2. All is yours when faith up-holds you, Sets your won-drous spir-it free;
3. All is yours, oh, bless-ed knowl-edge! Like the sands be-side the sea,

Heav'n un-locks her rich-est treas-ure For your wait-ing eyes to see.
For the might-y One has prom-ised He your all in all will be.
Or the drops with-in its wa-ters, Shall your man-y con-quests be.

236   Be Ye Prospered

WRIGHT FIELD

FRANGKISER

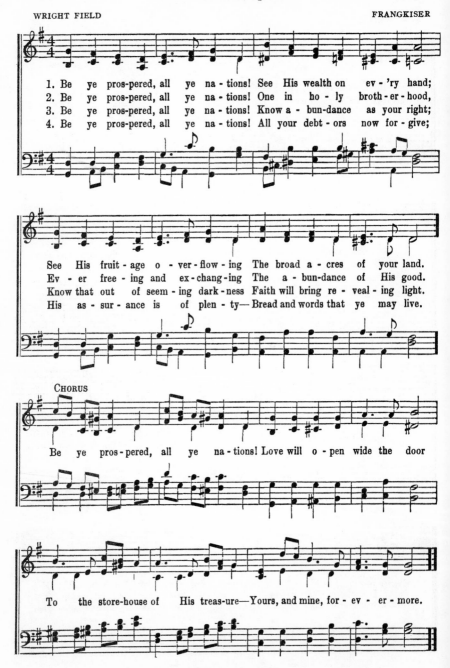

1. Be ye pros-pered, all ye na - tions! See His wealth on ev - 'ry hand;
2. Be ye pros-pered, all ye na - tions! One in ho - ly broth - er - hood,
3. Be ye pros-pered, all ye na - tions! Know a - bun-dance as your right;
4. Be ye pros-pered, all ye na - tions! All your debt - ors now for - give;

See His fruit - age o - ver - flow - ing The broad a - cres of your land.
Ev - er free - ing and ex - chang-ing The a - bun-dance of His good.
Know that out of seem - ing dark - ness Faith will bring re - veal - ing light.
His as - sur - ance is of plen - ty— Bread and words that ye may live.

CHORUS

Be ye pros-pered, all ye na - tions! Love will o - pen wide the door

To the store-house of His treas-ure—Yours, and mine, for - ev - er - more.

237 In God We Trust

F. B. WHITNEY

CARL JEAN TOLMAN

1. In all things in God we trust, For His cause is al - ways just;
2. In all things in God we trust, Trust in Him we will, we must—
3. In all things in God we trust; He will all af - fairs ad - just;

'Tis His will that we should share In His bless - ings rich and rare.
True to prom - is - es He'll be For suc - cess, pros - per - i - ty—
On Him al - ways we re - ly For His boun - te - ous sup - ply.

Ev - er let us trust the good, Let His law be un - der - stood,
Nev - er giv - ing thought to lack, See - ing naught can hold us back,
Trust-ing thro' all age and clime, Trust-ing al - ways, thro' all time,

Know - ing that we can - not fail, That His good will e'er pre - vail.
Ev - er for - ward, faith - ful, true, Count-ing ev - 'ry bless - ing new.
Trust - ing, see - ing, year by year More of bless - ings that ap - pear.

I'm Rich in Thee

RUSSEL KEMP

FRANGKISER

1. There is no lack, no pov-er-ty: Thy well of plen-ty flows for me.
2. Lord, I would feel Thy sub-stance fine, En-rich my soul with wealth di-vine,
3. I have re-ceived, I thank Thee, Lord, My soul with heav'n-ly wealth is stored,

What-e'er I do, what-e'er I see, There is no lack: I'm rich in Thee.
So bless my words that I may see There is no lack: I'm rich in Thee.
All praise to Thee, all praise to Thee; There is no lack: I'm rich in Thee.

CHORUS

I'm rich in Thee, I'm rich in Thee, Thy well of plen-ty flows for me,

Thy wealth of sub-stance now I see; There is no lack: I'm rich in Thee.

239 Peace, Sweet Peace

LUTHER LORENTZ

LUTHER LORENTZ

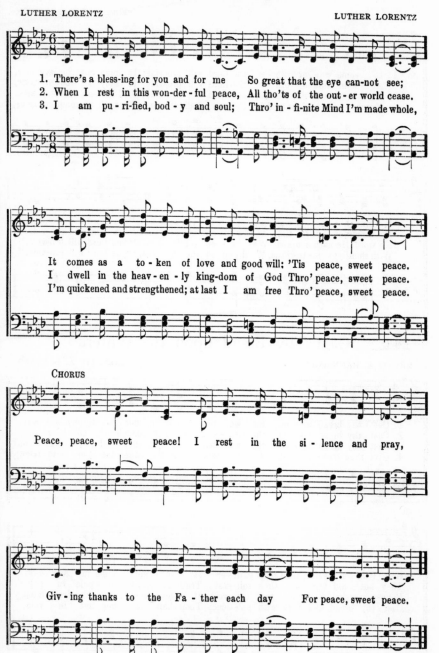

1. There's a bless-ing for you and for me   So great that the eye can-not see;
2. When I rest in this won-der-ful peace,   All tho'ts of the out-er world cease.
3. I   am pu-ri-fied, bod-y and soul;   Thro' in-fi-nite Mind I'm made whole,

It comes as a to-ken of love and good will; 'Tis peace, sweet   peace.
I dwell in the heav-en-ly king-dom of God Thro' peace, sweet   peace.
I'm quickened and strengthened; at last I   am free Thro' peace, sweet   peace.

Chorus

Peace, peace, sweet   peace! I rest   in   the   si-lence and   pray,

Giv-ing thanks to the Fa-ther each day   For peace, sweet peace.

240 The Lord Will Provide

PROF. S. C. HARRINGTON

1. In some way or oth-er the Lord will pro-vide; It may not be *my* way,
2. At some time or oth-er the Lord will pro-vide; It may not be *my* time,
3. De-spond then no lon-ger; the Lord will pro-vide; And this be the to-ken:
4. March on, then, right bold-ly; the sea shall di-vide, The path be made glo-rious;

It may not be *thy* way, And yet in His *own* way "the Lord will pro-vide."
It may not be *thy* time, And yet in His *own* time "the Lord will pro-vide."
No word He hath spo-ken Was ev-er yet bro-ken—"The Lord will pro-vide."
With shoutings vic-to-rio us, We'll join in the cho-rus, "The Lord will pro-vide."

241 Cast Thy Bread upon the Waters

MRS. P. A. HANNAFORD CHARLOTTE A. BARNARD

1. Cast thy bread up-on the wa-ters, Think-ing not 'tis thrown a-way;
2. Cast thy bread up-on the wa-ters: Wild-ly though the bil-lows roll,
3. Cast thy bread up-on the wa-ters; Why wilt thou still doubt-ing stand?
4. Give thou free-ly of thy sub-stance—O'er this cause the Lord doth reign;

God Him-self saith, thou shalt gath-er It a-gain some fu-ture day.
They but aid thee as thou toil-est Truth to spread from pole to pole.
Boun-teous shall God send the har-vest, If thou sow with lib-'ral hand.
Cast thy bread, and work with pa-tience, Thou shalt la-bor not in vain.

242 Like a River Glorious

FRANCES R. HAVERGAL

J. BARNBY

1. Like a riv-er glo-rious Is God's per-fect peace,
2. Hid-den in the hol-low Of His bless-ed hand,
3. We may trust Him sole-ly All for us to do;

O-ver all vic-to-rious In its bright in-crease.
Nev-er foe can fol-low, Nev-er trai-tor stand.
They who trust Him whol-ly, Find Him whol-ly true.

Per-fect—yet it flow-eth Full-er ev-'ry day;
Not a surge of wor-ry, Not a shade of care,
Stayed up-on Je-ho-vah, Hearts are ful-ly blest,

Per-fect—yet it grow-eth Deep-er all the way.
Not a blast of hur-ry Touch the spir-it there.
Find-ing, as He prom-ised, Per-fect peace and rest.

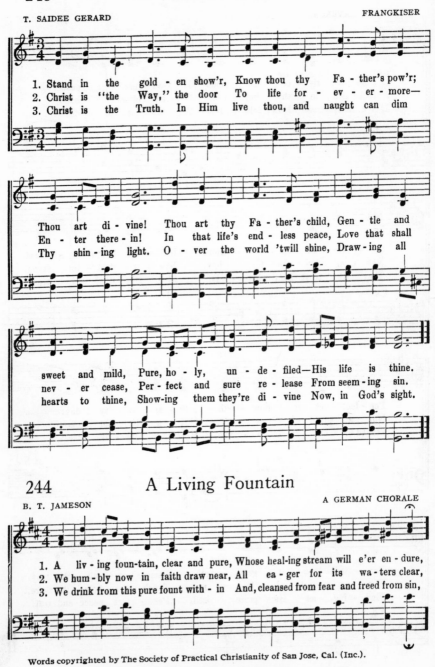

243

Know Thou

T. SAIDEE GERARD

FRANGKISER

1. Stand in the gold - en show'r, Know thou thy Fa - ther's pow'r;
2. Christ is "the Way," the door To life for - ev - er - more—
3. Christ is the Truth. In Him live thou, and naught can dim

Thou art di - vine! Thou art thy Fa - ther's child, Gen - tle and
En - ter there - in! In that life's end - less peace, Love that shall
Thy shin - ing light. O - ver the world 'twill shine, Draw - ing all

sweet and mild, Pure, ho - ly, un - de - filed—His life is thine.
nev - er cease, Per - fect and sure re - lease From seem - ing sin.
hearts to thine, Show - ing them they're di - vine Now, in God's sight.

244

A Living Fountain

B. T. JAMESON

A GERMAN CHORALE

1. A liv - ing foun - tain, clear and pure, Whose heal - ing stream will e'er en - dure,
2. We hum - bly now in faith draw near, All ea - ger for its wa - ters clear,
3. We drink from this pure fount with - in And, cleansed from fear and freed from sin,

A Living Fountain

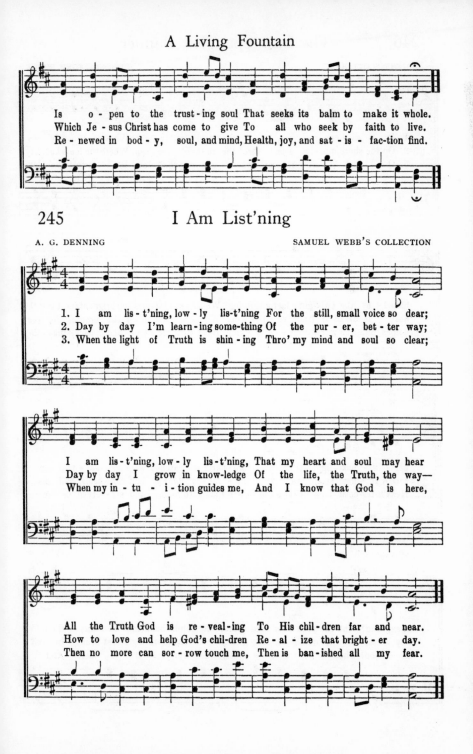

Is o - pen to the trust - ing soul That seeks its balm to make it whole.
Which Je - sus Christ has come to give To all who seek by faith to live.
Re - newed in bod - y, soul, and mind, Health, joy, and sat - is - fac-tion find.

245   I Am List'ning

A. G. DENNING

SAMUEL WEBB'S COLLECTION

1. I am lis - t'ning, low - ly lis-t'ning For the still, small voice so dear;
2. Day by day I'm learn-ing some-thing Of the pur - er, bet - ter way;
3. When the light of Truth is shin - ing Thro' my mind and soul so clear;

I am lis - t'ning, low - ly lis-t'ning, That my heart and soul may hear
Day by day I grow in know-ledge Of the life, the Truth, the way—
When my in - tu - i - tion guides me, And I know that God is here,

All the Truth God is re - veal-ing To His chil - dren far and near.
How to love and help God's chil-dren Re - al - ize that bright - er day.
Then no more can sor - row touch me, Then is ban-ished all my fear.

The Star-Spangled Banner

FRANCIS SCOTT KEY

JOHN STAFFORD SMITH

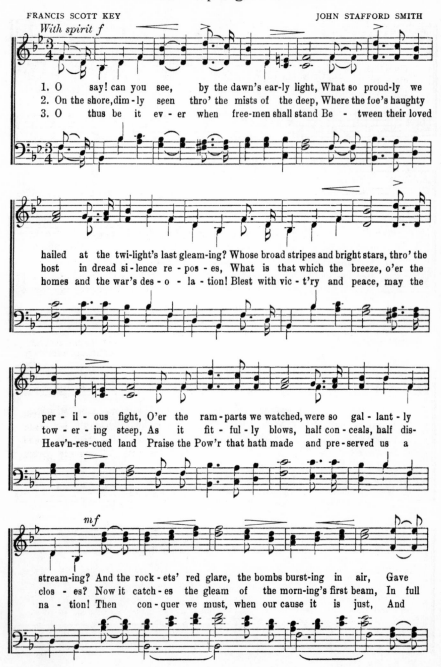

1. O say! can you see, by the dawn's ear-ly light, What so proud-ly we
2. On the shore, dim-ly seen thro' the mists of the deep, Where the foe's haughty
3. O thus be it ev-er when free-men shall stand Be-tween their loved

hailed at the twi-light's last gleam-ing? Whose broad stripes and bright stars, thro' the
host in dread si-lence re-pos-es, What is that which the breeze, o'er the
homes and the war's des-o-la-tion! Blest with vic-t'ry and peace, may the

per-il-ous fight, O'er the ram-parts we watched, were so gal-lant-ly
tow-er-ing steep, As it fit-ful-ly blows, half con-ceals, half dis-
Heav'n-res-cued land Praise the Pow'r that hath made and pre-served us a

stream-ing? And the rock-ets' red glare, the bombs burst-ing in air, Gave
clos-es? Now it catch-es the gleam of the morn-ing's first beam, In full
na-tion! Then con-quer we must, when our cause it is just, And

The Star-Spangled Banner

CHORUS *f*

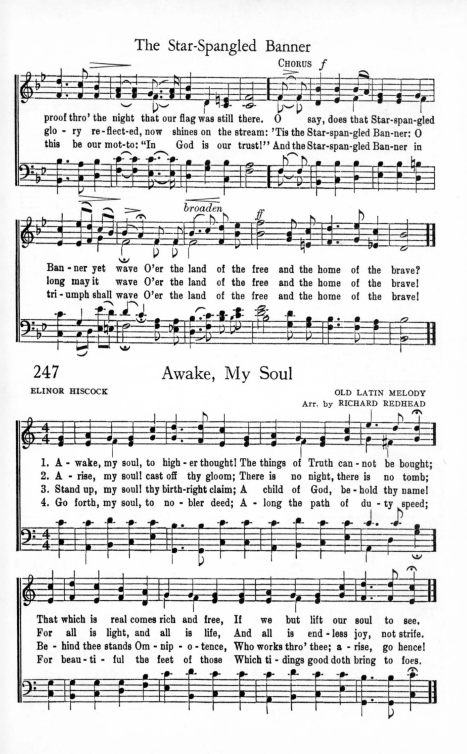

proof thro' the night that our flag was still there. O say, does that Star-span-gled
glo - ry re - flect-ed, now shines on the stream: 'Tis the Star-span-gled Ban-ner: O
this be our mot-to: "In God is our trust!" And the Star-span-gled Ban-ner in

broaden   *ff*

Ban - ner yet wave O'er the land of the free and the home of the brave?
long may it wave O'er the land of the free and the home of the brave!
tri - umph shall wave O'er the land of the free and the home of the brave!

247 Awake, My Soul

ELINOR HISCOCK

OLD LATIN MELODY
Arr. by RICHARD REDHEAD

1. A - wake, my soul, to high - er thought! The things of Truth can - not be bought;
2. A - rise, my soul! cast off thy gloom; There is no night, there is no tomb;
3. Stand up, my soul! thy birth-right claim; A child of God, be - hold thy name!
4. Go forth, my soul, to no - bler deed; A - long the path of du - ty speed;

That which is real comes rich and free, If we but lift our soul to see.
For all is light, and all is life, And all is end - less joy, not strife.
Be - hind thee stands Om - nip - o - tence, Who works thro' thee; a - rise, go hence!
For beau - ti - ful the feet of those Which ti - dings good doth bring to foes.

248 Thou Lord of Life

SAMUEL LONGFELLOW

GERMAN MELODY
Arr. by SAMUEL DYER

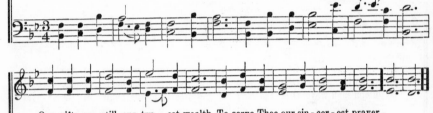

1. Thou Lord of life, our sav - ing health, Who mak'st Thy suf-f'ring ones our care,
2. As on the riv - er's ris - ing tide Flow strength and coolness from the sea,
3. To heal the wound, to still the pain, And strength to fail - ing puls - es bring,
4. Bless Thou the gifts our hands have brought; Bless Thou the work our heart has planned:

Our gifts are still our tru - est wealth, To serve Thee our sin - cer - est prayer.
So, thro' the ways our hands pro - vide, May quick'ning life flow in from Thee.
Un - til the lame shall leap a - gain, And the parched lips with gladness sing.
Ours is the faith, the will, the tho't; The rest, O God, is in Thy hand. A - men.

249 We Feel the Heart of Silence

JOHN G. WHITTIER

S. S. WESLEY

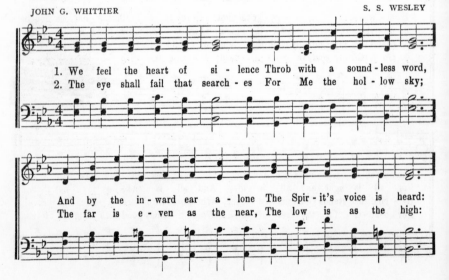

1. We feel the heart of si - lence Throb with a sound - less word,
2. The eye shall fail that search - es For Me the hol - low sky;

And by the in - ward ear a - lone The Spir - it's voice is heard:
The far is e - ven as the near, The low is as the high:

We Feel the Heart of Silence

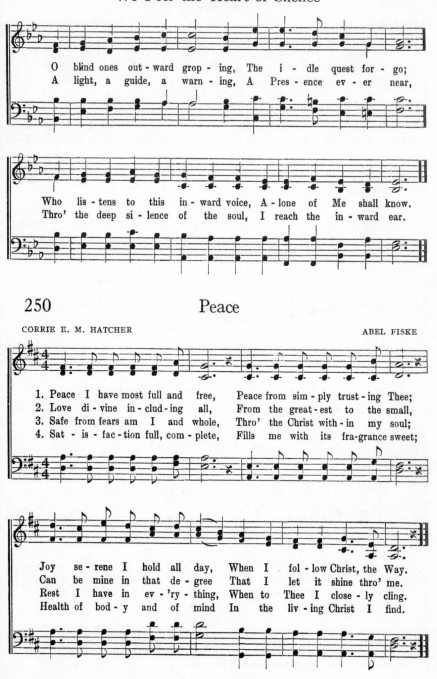

O blind ones out-ward grop-ing, The i-dle quest for-go;
A light, a guide, a warn-ing, A Pres-ence ev-er near,

Who lis-tens to this in-ward voice, A-lone of Me shall know.
Thro' the deep si-lence of the soul, I reach the in-ward ear.

250   Peace

CORRIE E. M. HATCHER   ABEL FISKE

1. Peace I have most full and free, Peace from sim-ply trust-ing Thee;
2. Love di-vine in-clud-ing all, From the great-est to the small,
3. Safe from fears am I and whole, Thro' the Christ with-in my soul;
4. Sat-is-fac-tion full, com-plete, Fills me with its fra-grance sweet;

Joy se-rene I hold all day, When I fol-low Christ, the Way.
Can be mine in that de-gree That I let it shine thro' me.
Rest I have in ev-'ry-thing, When to Thee I close-ly cling.
Health of bod-y and of mind In the liv-ing Christ I find.

O That Will Be Glory

C. H. G.

CHARLES H. GABRIEL

1. When all my la - bors and tri - als are o'er, And I am safe on that beau - ti - ful shore, Just to be near the dear Lord I a - dore, Will thro' the a - ges be glo - ry for me.......

2 When, by the gift of His in - fi - nite grace, I am ac - cord - ed in heav - en a place, Just to be there and to look on His face,

3. Friends will be there I have loved long a - go; Joy like a riv - er a - round me will flow; Yet just a smile from my Sav - ior, I know,

rit.

CHORUS *Faster*

O that will be O............ that will

glo - ry for me, Glo - ry for me, glo - ry for me; When by His grace

be glo - ry for me, glo - ry for me, glo - ry for me;........

rit.

I shall look on His face, That will be glo - ry, be glo - ry for me.

Copyright, 1928, renewal. Homer A. Rodeheaver, owner

252   Oh! That Is Now Glory for Me

(Words by MYRTLE FILLMORE. *Music on opposite page)*

1 Banished all burdens of sorrow and pain,
  My soul's aglow with an infinite flame;
  My voice, exultant, now sings this refrain,
  Anthem of glory, oh, glory for me.

CHORUS—Oh! that is now glory for me,
         Glory for me, glory for me!
         For by His grace, I now look on His face;
         That is my glory, oh, glory for me!

2 Life, like a river of infinite grace,
  Mirrors the light of His glorious face,
  Making of earth a most heavenly place
  Filled with His presence, oh, glory for me!

253   I Will Lift Mine Eyes

Psalm 121, paraphrased
by B. T. JAMESON

A. H. MANN

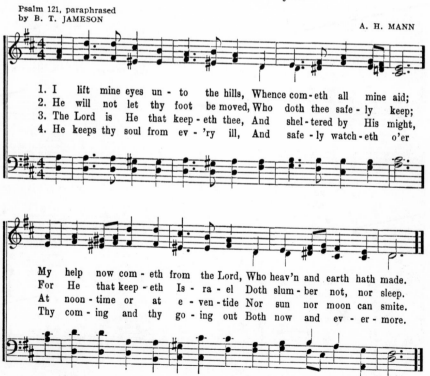

1. I lift mine eyes un - to the hills, Whence com - eth all mine aid;
2. He will not let thy foot be moved, Who doth thee safe - ly keep;
3. The Lord is He that keep - eth thee, And shel - tered by His might,
4. He keeps thy soul from ev - 'ry ill, And safe - ly watch - eth o'er

My help now com - eth from the Lord, Who heav'n and earth hath made.
For He that keep - eth Is - ra - el Doth slum - ber not, nor sleep.
At noon - time or at e - ven - tide Nor sun nor moon can smite.
Thy com - ing and thy go - ing out Both now and ev - er - more.

Keep the Heart Singing

C. H. G.

CHARLES H. GABRIEL

1. We may light-en toil and care, Or a heav-y bur-den share, With a
2. If His love is in the soul And we yield to His con-trol, Sweet-est
3. How a word of love will cheer, Kin-dle hope, and ban-ish fear, Soothe a

word, a kind-ly deed, or sun-ny smile; We may gir-dle day and night
mu-sic will the lone-ly hours be-guile; We may drive the clouds a-way,
pain, or take a-way the sting of guile; Oh, how much we all may do

FINE.

With a ha-lo of de-light, If we keep the heart sing-ing all the while.
Cheer and bless the dark-est day, If we keep the heart sing-ing all the while.
In the world we trav-el thro', If we keep the heart sing-ing all the while.

CHORUS

Keep the heart sing-ing all the while;........ Make the world brighter with a
sing-ing, sing-ing all the while; bright-er,

D. S.

smile;........ Keep the song ring-ing! lone-ly hours we may be-guile. A-men.
bright-er with a smile;

255 Wonderful Peace

REV. W. D. CORNELL. Alt.

REV. W. G. COOPER

1. Far a-way in the depths of my spir-it to-night Rolls a
2. What a treas-ure I have in this won-der-ful peace, Bur-ied
3. I am rest-ing to-night in this won-der-ful peace, Rest-ing

mel - o - dy sweet-er than psalm; In ce - les - tial - like strains it un-
deep in the heart of my soul; So se - cure that no pow - er can
sweet-ly in Je - sus' con - trol; For I'm kept from all dan - ger by

ceas - ing - ly falls O'er my soul like an in - fi - nite calm.
mine it a - way While the years of e - ter - ni - ty roll.
night and by day, And His glo - ry is flood - ing my soul.

CHORUS

Peace! peace! won - der - ful peace, Com-ing down from the Fa - ther a - bove; Sweep

o - ver my spir - it for - ev - er, I pray, In fath-om-less bil-lows of love.

256 I'll Go Where You Want Me to Go

MARY BROWN

CARRIE E. ROUNSEFELL

1. It may not be on the moun-tain height, Or o - ver the storm - y sea,
2. Per-haps to-day there are lov - ing words Which Je-sus would have me speak;
3. There's sure-ly some-where a low - ly place In earth's har-vest fields so wide,

It may not be at the bat - tle's front My Lord will have need of me;
There may be now in the paths of sin Some wan-d'rer whom I should seek:
Where I may la - bor thro' life's short day For Je - sus, the Cru - ci - fied.

But if by a still, small voice He calls To paths that I do not know,
O Sav - ior, if Thou wilt be my guide, Tho' dark and rug-ged the way,
So trust-ing my all to Thy ten - der care, And know-ing Thou lov - est me,

I'll an-swer, dear Lord, with my hand in Thine, I'll go where You want me to go.
My voice shall ech - o the mes-sage sweet, I'll say what You want me to say.
I'll do Thy will with a heart sin - cere, I'll be what You want me to be.

REFRAIN

I'll go where You want me to go, dear Lord, O-ver mountain, or plain, or sea;

I'll Go Where You Want Me to Go

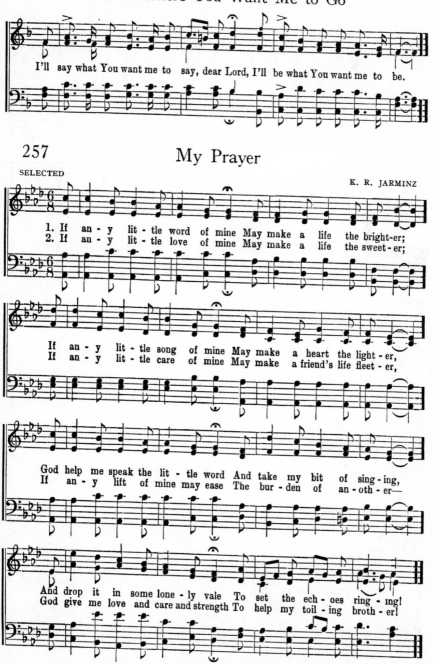

I'll say what You want me to say, dear Lord, I'll be what You want me to be.

257

My Prayer

SELECTED

K. R. JARMINZ

1. If an - y lit - tle word of mine May make a life the bright-er;
2. If an - y lit - tle love of mine May make a life the sweet-er;

If an - y lit - tle song of mine May make a heart the light - er,
If an - y lit - tle care of mine May make a friend's life fleet - er,

God help me speak the lit - tle word And take my bit of sing - ing,
If an - y lift of mine may ease The bur - den of an - oth - er—

And drop it in some lone - ly vale To set the ech - oes ring - ing!
God give me love and care and strength To help my toil - ing broth - er!

258 More Like the Master

C. H. G.

CHARLES H. GABRIEL

1. More like the Mas-ter I would ev-er be, More of His meek-ness,
2. More like the Mas-ter is my dai-ly prayer; More strength to car-ry
3. More like the Mas-ter I would live and grow; More of His love to

more hu-mil-i-ty; More zeal to la-bor, more cour-age to be true,
cross-es I must bear; More ear-nest ef-fort to bring His king-dom in;
oth-ers I would show; More self-de-ni-al like His in Gal-i-lee,

rit. CHORUS

More con-se-cra-tion for work He bids me do........... Take Thou my
More of His Spir-it the wan-der-er to win..........
More like the Mas-ter I long to ev-er be........... Take my heart, O

heart,.... I would be Thine a-lone;...... Take Thou my heart..... and
take my heart, I would be Thine a-lone; Take my heart, O take my heart and

More Like the Master

make it all Thine own;..... Purge me from sin,..... O Lord, I now im-
make it all Thine own; Purge Thou me from ev-'ry sin, O Lord, I

plore,..... Wash me and keep...... me Thine for - ev - er - more.
now im-plore, Wash and keep, O wash and keep me Thine for - ev - er - more.

259 More Love to Thee

ELIZABETH PRENTISS

W. H. DOANE

1. More love to Thee, O Christ, More love to Thee! Hear Thou the
2. Once earth-ly joy I craved, Sought peace and rest; Now Thee a-
3. Then shall my lat - est breath Whis - per Thy praise; This be the

prayer I make On bend - ed knee; This is my ear - nest plea:
lone I seek, Give what is best; This all my prayer shall be:
part - ing cry My heart shall raise; This still its prayer shall be:

More love, O Christ, to Thee, More love to Thee, More love to Thee!

River of Healing

NEIL McGINNESS

FRANGKISER

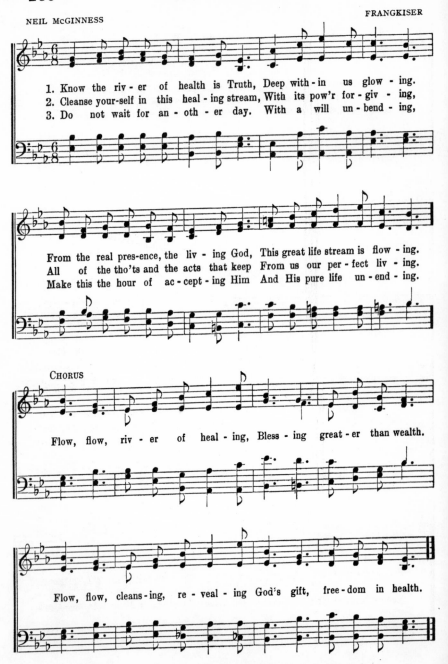

1. Know the riv-er of health is Truth, Deep with-in us glow-ing.
2. Cleanse your-self in this heal-ing stream, With its pow'r for-giv-ing,
3. Do not wait for an-oth-er day. With a will un-bend-ing,

From the real pres-ence, the liv-ing God, This great life stream is flow-ing.
All of the tho'ts and the acts that keep From us our per-fect liv-ing.
Make this the hour of ac-cept-ing Him And His pure life un-end-ing.

CHORUS

Flow, flow, riv-er of heal-ing, Bless-ing great-er than wealth.

Flow, flow, cleans-ing, re-veal-ing God's gift, free-dom in health.

261   What a Friend

JOSEPH SCRIVEN

CHARLES C. CONVERSE

1. What a friend we have in Je - sus, All our sins and griefs to bear!
2. Have we tri - als and temp-ta - tions? Is there troub-le an - y - where?
3. Are we weak and heav - y - la - den, Cum-bered with a load of care?—

What a priv - i - lege to car - ry Ev - 'ry-thing to God in prayer!
We should nev - er be dis - cour - aged, Take it to the Lord in prayer.
Pre - cious Sav - ior, still our ref - uge— Take it to the Lord in prayer.

O what peace we oft - en for - feit, O what need-less pain we bear,
Can we find a friend so faith - ful Who will all our sor - rows share?
Do thy friends de - spise, for - sake thee? Take it to the Lord in prayer;

All be - cause we do not car - ry Ev - 'ry-thing to God in prayer!
Je - sus knows our ev - 'ry weak - ness, Take it to the Lord in prayer.
In His arms He'll take and shield thee, Thou wilt find a sol - ace there.

262   Live for Something

ANONYMOUS

WILLIAM BOYCE

1. Live for some-thing, be not i - dle, Look a - bout thee for em - ploy;
2. Fold-ed hands are ev - er wea - ry, Self - ish hearts are nev - er gay;
3. Scat-ter bless - ings on your path-way, Gen - tle words and cheer - ing smiles;
4. As the pleas - ant sun-shine fall - eth Ev - er on the grate - ful earth,

Sit not down to use - less dream-ing, La - bor is the sweet-est joy.
Life for thee hath man - y du - ties, Ac - tive be, then, while you may.
Bet - ter far than gold and sil - ver Are their grief-dis - pel - ling wiles.
So let sym - pa - thy and kind-ness Glad-den well the dark-ened earth.

263   Let

V. M. J.

VIVA M. JANUARY

1. Let God's own love now fill my heart, Let ev - 'ry
2. Let strength and cour - - age fill my soul, Let ev - 'ry
3. Let bod - y, soul, and spir - it be Now con - se-

doubt and fear de - part, Let Om - ni - pres - ence with me
bur - - den from me roll, Let wis - dom help me to un-
cra - - ted all to Thee. Let all my life blend with Thy

Let

stay   And   bless   and   cheer   and guide   my   way.
fold   True free - dom,   peace,   and   joy   un - told.
will   And   say   to   self,   Peace, peace, be   still.

264   Bon Voyage

ERNEST C. WILSON   FRANGKISER

1. I send my dream ships gai - ly Out on the mind's broad sea;
2. And Cap - tain, guide my choos-ing That what I   ask   of   Thee

O thought winds, treat them kind - ly   And give them back to me.
May make a wor - thy car - go   As   it   re - turns to me.

And, O winds, speed them on - ward   A - round their cir - cled track,
And when my dream ships an - chor, Re - turned from far - off sea,

And, O sea,   bear them safe - ly; And may they noth - ing lack.
All my tho'ts I'll find pic - tured In what they bring to me.

265 God Be with You Till We Meet Again

J. E. RANKIN

W. G. TOMER

1. God be with you till we meet a - gain; By His coun - sels guide, up-
2. God be with you till we meet a - gain; 'Neath His wings pro - tect - ing
3. God be with you till we meet a - gain; When life's per - ils thick con-
4. God be with you till we meet a - gain; Keep love's ban - ner float - ing

hold you, With His sheep se - cure - ly fold you; God be
hide you, Dai - ly man - na still pro - vide you; God be
found you, Put His arms un - fail - ing round you; God be
o'er you; It will com - fort and pro - tect you; God be

CHORUS

with you till we meet a - gain. Till we meet, ... till we meet,

Till we meet at Je - sus' feet; Till we meet, ... till we

meet, God be with you till we meet a - gain. A - men.

Happy Sunshine

FRANCIS J. GABLE

FRANGKISER

Brightly

1. There is sun - shine all a - bout me, In my heart and in my
2. Hap - py sun - shine brings me glad - ness, I am hap - py all the

face; It is shin - ing, shin - ing, shin - ing, For there's
while; And my friends can see the sun - shine, For it's

sun - shine ev - 'ry place....... I'm in sun - shine, hap - py
shin - ing in my smile.......

CHORUS

sun - shine, And its rays are warm and bright; I'm in

sun - shine, hap - py sun - shine, And I'm hap - py in its light.

Our Sunday School

FRANCIS J. GABLE

FRANGKISER

Marcia

1. We are loy-al to our Sun-day school, Our best ef-forts we are giv - ing;
2. We are bus-y in our Sun-day school, Spir-it's les-sons we are learn - ing;
3. We are hap-py in our Sun-day school, Songs of gladness we are sing - ing;

As we think a-right, God's pure ho - ly light Beams in our dai - ly liv - ing.
Gleams of truth di - vine in our fac - es shine, Love for the Fa - ther burn - ing.
We our voic - es raise in our notes of praise, Joy in our hearts is spring - ing.

CHORUS

In the on-ward march of the sons of God We are al-ways in the van;

We are proud and glad that we have a part In the lov-ing Fa-ther's plan,

As we read His word, as we learn His will, As we keep the Gold-en Rule,

Our Sunday School

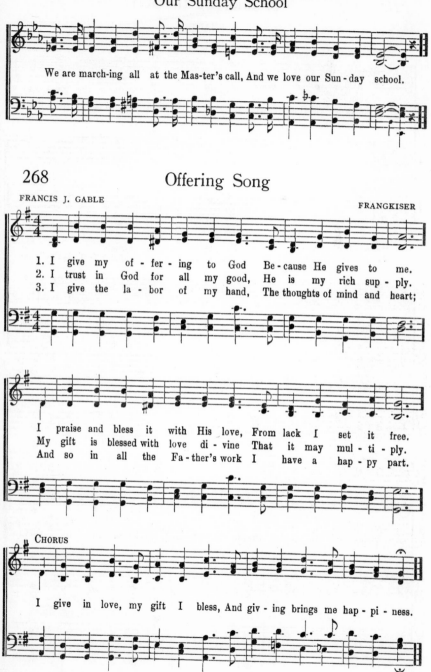

We are march-ing all at the Mas-ter's call, And we love our Sun-day school.

268   Offering Song

FRANCIS J. GABLE

FRANGKISER

1. I give my of-fer-ing to God Be-cause He gives to me.
2. I trust in God for all my good, He is my rich sup-ply.
3. I give the la-bor of my hand, The thoughts of mind and heart;

I praise and bless it with His love, From lack I set it free.
My gift is blessed with love di-vine That it may mul-ti-ply.
And so in all the Fa-ther's work I have a hap-py part.

CHORUS

I give in love, my gift I bless, And giv-ing brings me hap-pi-ness.

269 Thanks Be to God

CHANT

ANONYMOUS

Thanks be to God for His gift of rich - es, Thanks be to God for His

gift of joy, Thanks be to God for His gift of health,

Thanks be to God, thanks be to God, Thanks be to God.

270 Birthday greeting

ELEANOR ALLEN SCHROLL. JOSEPH BARNBY

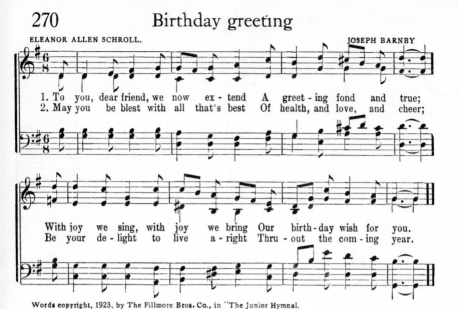

1. To you, dear friend, we now ex-tend A greet-ing fond and true;
2. May you be blest with all that's best Of health, and love, and cheer;

With joy we sing, with joy we bring Our birth-day wish for you.
Be your de-light to live a-right Thru-out the com-ing year.

Words copyright, 1923, by The Fillmore Bros. Co., in "The Junior Hymnal.

271 God speaks to us in bird and song

JOSEPH JOHNSON LOUIS LE SAINT

1. God speaks to us in bird and song; In winds that drift the clouds a-long;
2. God speaks to us in far and near, In peace of home and friends so dear;
3. God speaks to us in dark-est night; By qui-et ways thru morn-ings bright,
4. God speaks to us in ev-'ry land, On wave-lapped shore and si-lent strand;

A-bove the din of toil and wrong,—A mel-o-dy of love,
From out the past, and pres-ent clear, A mel-o-dy of love
When shad-ows fall with eve-ning light, A mel-o-dy of love.
By kiss of child, and touch of hand, A mel-o-dy of love.

Music copyright, 1920, by The Fillmore Bros. Co., in "Hymns for Today." International copyright.

272 The spring-tide hour

JOHN S. B. MONSELL, alt.

JOSEPH BARNBY

1. The spring - tide hour Brings leaf and flow'r, With songs of life and love;
2. Bird, flow'r and tree Seem to a - gree Their choic - est gifts to bring;
3. Lord, let Thy love, Fresh from a - bove, Soft as the south wind blow,
4. And when Thy voice Makes earth re - joice—The hills to laugh and sing;

And ma - ny a lay Wears out the day In ma - ny a leaf - y grove.
And this my pray'r, My heart may share The won-drous joys of spring.
Call forth its bloom, Wake its per-fume, And bid its spi - ces flow.
Lord, teach this heart To bear its part, And join the praise of spring.

273 Beautiful season of joy

ELEANOR ALLEN SCHROLL.

RUBINSTEIN. Arr. by HENRY FILLMORE

1. Beau - ti - ful sea - son of joy ev - 'ry-where, Earth is a - wak - ing,
2. Beau - ti - ful flow - ers all spar - kling with dew, O'er all the beau - ty,
3. Mu - sic of brook - let and bree - zes and birds Rings in the wood-land,

heav - en is near; Voi - ces of na - ture with rap - ture de - clare,
skies smil - ing clear; God's wondrous good - ness and love shin - ing thru,
car - ols of cheer; This is the theme of the song with - out words,

Beautiful season of joy

Spring-time, glad spring-time is here. (*Omit.*) here.

274   Tell me the stories of Jesus

W. H. PARKER

F. A. CHALLINOR

1. Tell me the sto - ries of Je - sus I love to hear;
2. First let me hear how the chil - dren Stood round His knee;
3. In - to the cit - y I'd fol - low The chil - dren's band,
4. Tell me in ac - cents of won - der, How rolled the sea,

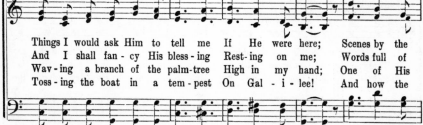

Things I would ask Him to tell me If He were here; Scenes by the
And I shall fan - cy His bless - ing Rest - ing on me; Words full of
Wav - ing a branch of the palm-tree High in my hand; One of His
Toss - ing the boat in a tem - pest On Gal - i - lee! And how the

rall.

way-side, Tales of the sea, Sto - ries of Je - sus, Tell them to me.
kind-ness, Deeds full of grace, All in the love-light Of Je - sus' face.
her - alds, Yes, I would sing Loud-est ho-san - nas! Je - sus is King.
Mas - ter, Read - y and kind, Chid - ed the bil - lows, And hushed the wind.

275 Dear Jesus take me as I am

LAURA WADE RICE, in C. E. World

J. H. FILLMORE

1. Dear Je - sus, take me as I am, And make me more like Thee,
2. Dear Je - sus, take these lips of mine, And may the words they say
3. Dear Je - sus, take my hands, my feet, To use for Thee, I pray;

Till, when God looks in - to my heart, Thine im - age He may see.
Be kind and gen - tle, pure and true, More Christ-like ev - 'ry day.
Help me to make this earth more sweet, More like to heav'n each day.

276 Help some one

GEORGIE TILLMAN SNEAD

J. H. FILLMORE

1. Would you make this dark world bright? Help some one; Do you wish the
2. There are souls op-pressed with care; Help some one; Sor - row, pain is
3. Put not du - ty i - dly by; Help some one; Ev - 'ry - where the

wrong made right? Help some one. Deeds, not words, are want - ed here; Love and
ev - 'ry-where; Help some one. Help to lift your broth-er's load, As He
need - y cry; Help some one. Far a - cross the roll - ing sea Men are

Help some one

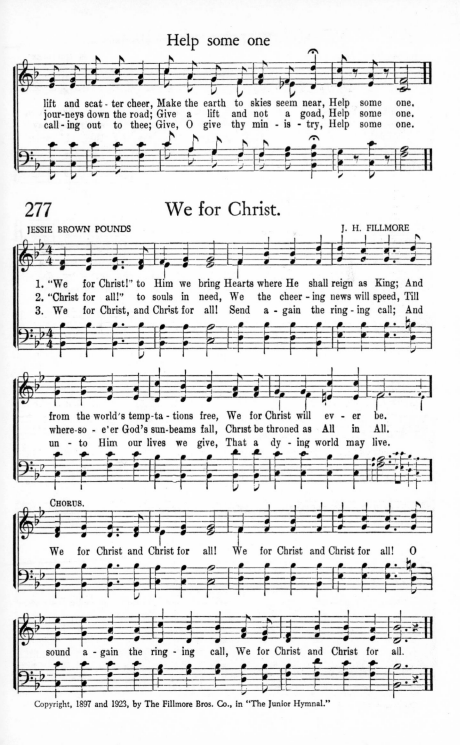

lift and scat-ter cheer, Make the earth to skies seem near, Help some one.
jour-neys down the road; Give a lift and not a goad, Help some one.
call-ing out to thee; Give, O give thy min-is-try, Help some one.

277 We for Christ.

JESSIE BROWN POUNDS

J. H. FILLMORE

1. "We for Christ!" to Him we bring Hearts where He shall reign as King; And
2. "Christ for all!" to souls in need, We the cheer-ing news will speed, Till
3. We for Christ, and Christ for all! Send a-gain the ring-ing call; And

from the world's temp-ta-tions free, We for Christ will ev-er be.
where-so-e'er God's sun-beams fall, Christ be throned as All in All.
un-to Him our lives we give, That a dy-ing world may live.

CHORUS.

We for Christ and Christ for all! We for Christ and Christ for all! O

sound a-gain the ring-ing call, We for Christ and Christ for all.

278 Serving the Lord with Gladness

JENNIE WILSON

J. H. FILLMORE

1. Walk in His way in the days of youth, Serv-ing the Lord with glad-ness;
2. Cast-ing a-side all your doubts and fears, Serv-ing the Lord with glad-ness;
3. Wher-ev-er bid-den, to la-bor go, Serv-ing the Lord with glad-ness;

Take for your guid-ance the word of Truth, Serv-ing the Lord with glad-ness.
Strive for the best in your ear-ly years, Serv-ing the Lord with glad-ness.
Seed for e-ter-ni-ty's har-vest sow, Serv-ing the Lord with glad-ness.

CHORUS

Serv - - - ing with glad - - ness, Serv - - - ing with glad-ness,
Serv-ing the Lord, serv-ing the Lord, Serv-ing the Lord with glad-ness,

rit.

Bless-ed are they who trust and o-bey, Serv-ing the Lord with glad-ness.

New arrangement copyright, 1923, by The Fillmore Bros. Co.

279 Who Made the Stars?

ANONYMOUS

J. H. FILLMORE

Unison

1. Who made the stars look out at night? Who gave the sun his heat and light?
2. Who gave each lit-tle bird a wing, And taught it how to fly and sing,
3. Who made each pret-ty blade of grass, With drops of dew, like beads of glass,
4. Who formed each heart His love to greet, For gifts of clothes, and food to eat?

Copyright 1911 and 1923, by The Fillmore Bros. Co., in "The Junior Hymnal"

Who Made the Stars?

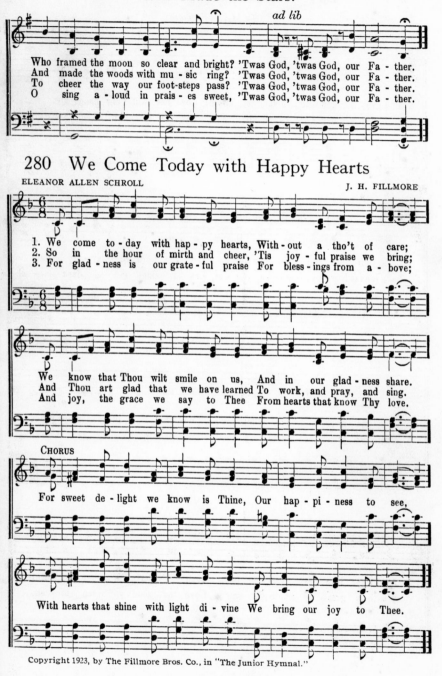

Who framed the moon so clear and bright? 'Twas God, 'twas God, our Fa - ther.
And made the woods with mu - sic ring? 'Twas God, 'twas God, our Fa - ther.
To cheer the way our foot-steps pass? 'Twas God, 'twas God, our Fa - ther.
O sing a - loud in prais - es sweet, 'Twas God, 'twas God, our Fa - ther.

280 We Come Today with Happy Hearts

ELEANOR ALLEN SCHROLL

J. H. FILLMORE

1. We come to - day with hap - py hearts, With - out a tho't of care;
2. So in the hour of mirth and cheer, 'Tis joy - ful praise we bring;
3. For glad - ness is our grate - ful praise For bless - ings from a - bove;

We know that Thou wilt smile on us, And in our glad - ness share.
And Thou art glad that we have learned To work, and pray, and sing.
And joy, the grace we say to Thee From hearts that know Thy love.

CHORUS

For sweet de - light we know is Thine, Our hap - pi - ness to see,

With hearts that shine with light di - vine We bring our joy to Thee.

281 Love the Good You See in All

(To Myrtle Fillmore)

LYDIA GARDINER WORTH

ERNST KROHR

With expression

1. Love is gen-tle, love is sweet, Love has will-ing hands and feet.
2. Love is nev-er cross and rude; Love is ev-er kind and good.

Love your work and love your play, Love the Lord of ev-'ry day;
Love makes hap-py, smil-ing fac-es, Let it shine in all dark plac-es!

Love the birds and love the flow'rs, Love the fresh, sweet morn-ing hours.
Wheth-er great or wheth-er small, Love the good you see in all;

rit.

Al-ways love to do your part, Then you'll have a hap-py heart.
Wheth-er great or wheth-er small, Love the good you see in all.

282   Ticktock

FRANCIS J. GABLE

FRANGKISER

The Redbird

M. E. L.

MAY E. LAWRENCE

Brightly

Once a lit - tle red - bird Sit - ting on a limb

Sang a mer - ry lit - tle song While I looked at him. "Cheer

up! cheer up," he seemed to say, "Be hap - py this bright sun - ny day."

rit.   *a tempo*

Then spread his wings and flew a - way, That hap - py lit - tle red - bird.

284
Like the Father

CARL FRANGKISER

FRANGKISER

1. I shall have on - ly thoughts of life, thoughts of life, thoughts of life,
2. I shall have on - ly thoughts of joy, thoughts of joy, thoughts of joy,

All be - cause I am like my Fa - ther, Who is joy - ous life.
All be - cause I am like my Fa - ther, Who is joy - ous life.

Chorus

Thoughts of life, thoughts of joy: I am like my Fa - ther!

Ev - 'ry girl, ev - 'ry boy Think - ing like the Fa - ther.

285 Love Song

SADIE M. THOMAS

EMORY L. COBLENTZ

1. Hap - py lit - tle chil - dren, Hap - py all day long, Do you know the se - cret
2. Jew - els for the crown - ing Of our bless - ed King; Hap - py lit - tle chil - dren,
3. Hap - py lit - tle chil - dren, On this ho - ly day Would you know the reason?
4. Love came down from heav - en Long, long time a - go; Do you then need won - der

REFRAIN

Of our hap - py song?
Joy - ous - ly we sing.
Lis - ten what we say.
Why we love Him so?

L - O - V - E, love, L - O - V - E, love, This is why we are so hap - py; L - O - V - E, love.

286 Luther's Cradle Hymn

M. L.

MARTIN LUTHER

1. A - way in a man - ger, No crib for a bed, The lit - tle Lord
3. The cat - tle are low - ing, The poor ba - by wakes, But lit - tle Lord

Je - sus Laid down His sweet head. The stars in the sky Looked
Je - sus, No cry - ing He makes; I love Thee, Lord Je - sus! Look

Luther's Cradle Hymn

down where He lay— The lit - tle Lord Je - sus, A - sleep on the hay.
down from the sky, And stay by my cra - dle To watch lul - la - by.

287   The Wondrous Story

FRANCIS J. GABLE

Moderato

FRANGKISER

1. Years a - go a proph - et old Told a won - drous sto - ry,
2. Love should dwell in ev - 'ry heart, None should harm his broth - er,

How the world of men should be Filled with peace and glo - ry.
All should live in peace and joy, Lov - ing one an - oth - er.

CHORUS

That's the tale we love to hear, The tale of Christ-mas morn,

When, to bring us joy and cheer, Christ our King was born.

288 I Open My Bible Book and Read

J. B. W.

JOHNIE B. WOOD

1. I o - pen my Bi - ble book and read: He loves me, He loves me.
2. I o - pen my Bi - ble book and read: He keeps me, He keeps me.
3. I o - pen my Bi - ble book and read: He helps me, He helps me.

289 Do You Know

CHRISTIANA CRONEMEYER

1. Do you know why I am glad On this morn - ing bright?

God is my Fa - ther, I am His child, And all is good and right.

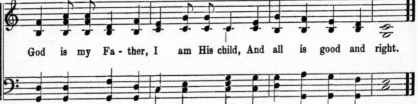

2 Do you know why I am glad
On this morning bright?

(Children fill in last two lines)

Why We're Happy

ROGER CARL

We will tell you in this song Why we're hap-py all day long.

In our work and in our play This is what we think each day:

Think - ing thoughts of kind - ness, Think - ing thoughts of love;

Think - ing thoughts of kind - ness, Think - ing thoughts of love.

291
Help One Another

REV. GEORGE F. HUNTING, D. D.

MRS. A. S. BARLOW, by per.

1. "Help one an - oth - er," the snow-flakes said, As they cud - dled down in their fleec - y bed, "One of us here would not be felt, One of us here would quick - ly melt;

2. "Help one an - oth - er," the ma - ple spray Said to its fel - low leaves one day, "The sun would with - er me here a - lone, Long e - nough ere the day is done;

3. "Help one an - oth - er," the dew - drop cried, See - ing an - oth - er drop close to its side, "This warm south breeze would dry me a - way, And I should be gone ere noon to - day;

4. "Help one an - oth - er," a grain of sand Said to an - oth - er grain just at hand, "The wind may car - ry me o - ver the sea, And then what would be - come of me?

Help One Another

But I'll help you, and you help me, And then what a great white
But I'll help you, and you help me, And then what a splen - did
But I'll help you, and you help me, And we'll make a brook, and
But broth - er, come, give me your hand, And we'll build a mon-u-ment and

1
2
Coda after fourth verse

drift we'll see."
shade there'll be." 5. And so the snow-flakes
run to the sea."
(*Omit*)..................) there we'll stand."

grew to drifts, The grains of sand to moun - tains, The

leaves be - came a pleas - ant shade, And dew-drops fed the foun - tains.

Sing a Song

CHRISTIANA CRONEMEYER

Moderato

1. When I go a - walk - ing and the sun is bright,
2. When the rain is fall - ing and the sky is gray,
3. Sing a song of night - time, time to go to bed.
4. When va - ca-tion's o - ver, and the school bells ring

Then I go a - sing - ing, for my heart is light.
Can - not go a - walk - ing— in the house I stay.
Play-time now is end - ed and our prayers are said.
Ting - a - ling - a - ling - ling, ting - a - ling - a - ling,

Sing a song of glad - ness all a - long the way;
Sing a song of rain - drops, for you see I know
When the dark-ness hides me and I can - not see,
Sing a song so joy - ous God will ev - er stay,

God is ev - er with me, and will keep me through the day.
God has sent the rain-drops down to make the flow - ers grow.
I am still not fright-ened, for I know God stays with me.
Give me wis-dom that I need for les - sons ev - 'ry day.

Closing Song

FRANCIS J. GABLE

FRANGKISER

Our Sun - day school is o - ver And to our homes we go,

To try to live like Je - sus And do the best we know.

We've learned a hap - py les - son A - bout God's love and joy,

And how His love brings heal - ing To ev - 'ry girl and boy.

294 Invocation

Andante

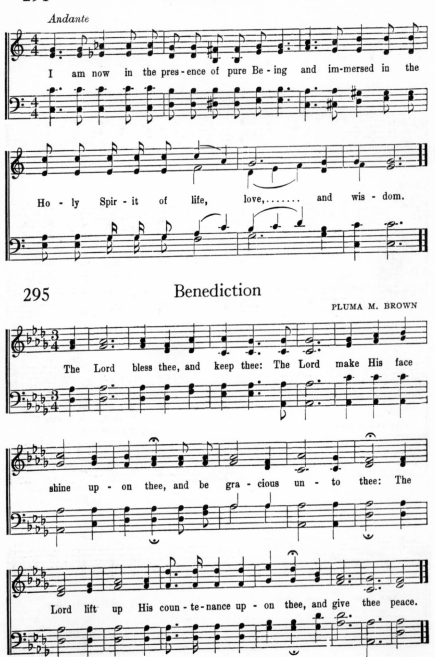

I am now in the pres-ence of pure Be-ing and im-mersed in the

Ho-ly Spir-it of life, love,....... and wis-dom.

295 Benediction

PLUMA M. BROWN

The Lord bless thee, and keep thee: The Lord make His face

shine up-on thee, and be gra-cious un-to thee: The

Lord lift up His coun-te-nance up-on thee, and give thee peace.

296

Double Amen (Dresden)

A - men, A - - - men.

297

Fivefold Amen

A - - - men, A - - men, A - - men, A - men, A - men.

298

Fourfold Amen

A - - - men, A - men, A - - - men, A - men.

299

Fourfold Amen

A - men, A - men, A - - - men, A - - - men.

300 Sevenfold Amen

JOHN STAINER

A - men, A - - - - - - men.

A - men, A - men, A - - - - - - - men.

A - - - - - - - - men.

A - - men.

A - - - men, A - - - men, A - - men.

A - - - men, A - - - - men, A - - men.

301 Holy, Holy

THOMAS BRIDGEWATER

Ho - ly, Ho - ly, Ho - ly, Lord God of hosts, Heaven and earth are

full of Thy glo - ry. Glo - ry be to Thee, O Lord, O Lord most high. A - men.

Be Merciful unto Us

C. W. BUTLER

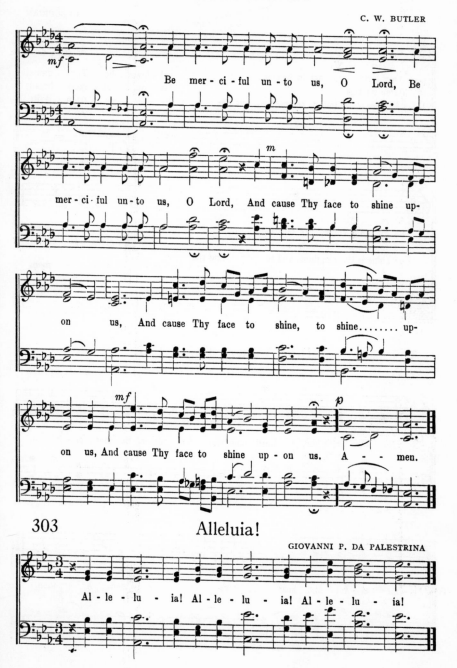

Be mer - ci - ful un - to us, O Lord, Be

mer - ci - ful un - to us, O Lord, And cause Thy face to shine up-

on us, And cause Thy face to shine, to shine........ up-

on us, And cause Thy face to shine up - on us. A - - men.

Alleluia!

GIOVANNI P. DA PALESTRINA

Al - le - lu - ia! Al - le - lu - ia! Al - le - lu - ia!

The Lord's Prayer

GREGORIAN

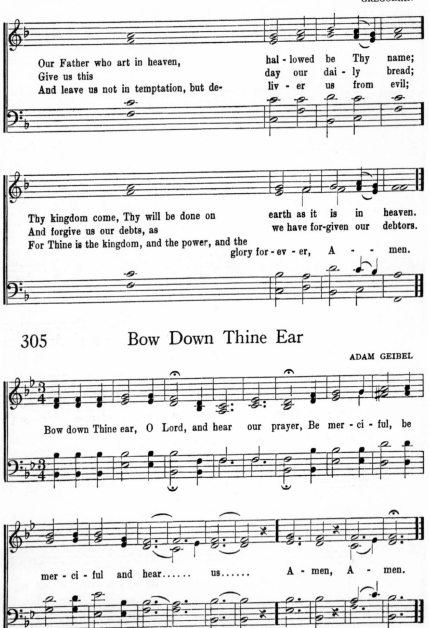

Our Father who art in heaven, hal - lowed be Thy name;
Give us this day our dai - ly bread;
And leave us not in temptation, but de- liv - er us from evil;

Thy kingdom come, Thy will be done on earth as it is in heaven.
And forgive us our debts, as we have for-given our debtors.
For Thine is the kingdom, and the power, and the glory for - ev - er, A - - men.

305 Bow Down Thine Ear

ADAM GEIBEL

Bow down Thine ear, O Lord, and hear our prayer, Be mer - ci - ful, be

mer - ci - ful and hear...... us...... A - men, A - men.

306 Let the Words of My Mouth

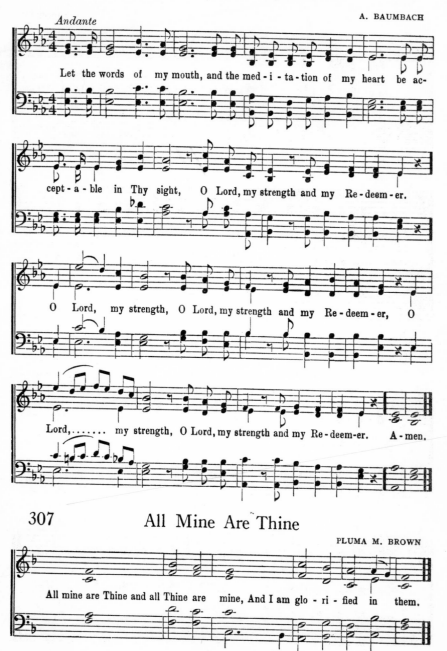

Let the words of my mouth, and the med - i - ta - tion of my heart be ac-
cept - a - ble in Thy sight, O Lord, my strength and my Re - deem - er.
O Lord, my strength, O Lord, my strength and my Re - deem - er, O
Lord,....... my strength, O Lord, my strength and my Re - deem - er. A - men.

307 All Mine Are Thine

PLUMA M. BROWN

All mine are Thine and all Thine are mine, And I am glo - ri - fied in them.

308

If I Be Lifted Up

PLUMA M. BROWN

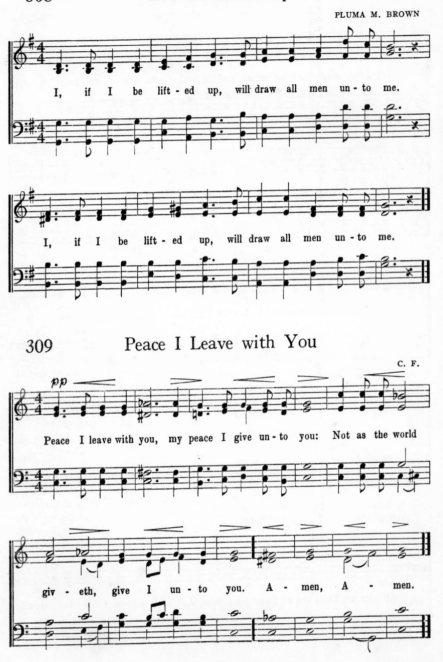

I, if I be lift-ed up, will draw all men un-to me.

I, if I be lift-ed up, will draw all men un-to me.

309

Peace I Leave with You

C. F.

Peace I leave with you, my peace I give un-to you: Not as the world

giv - eth, give I un - to you. A - men, A - men.

RESPONSIVE READING

310   The Lord's Prayer

Our Father who art in heaven, Hallowed be thy name. Thy kingdom come. Thy will be done in earth, as it is in heaven. Give us this day our daily bread. And forgive us our debts, as we also have forgiven our debtors. And leave us not in temptation, but deliver us from evil. For thine is the kingdom, and the power, and the glory, for ever. Amen.

311   Christmas

Though Christ a thousand times in
    Bethlehem be born,
If He's not born in thee, thy soul is
    all forlorn.
          —Angelus Silesius.

We behold in Jesus the Christ an illustration of the eternal Christ principle, the divine sonship of every one.

He that believeth on me, the works that I do shall he do also; and greater *works* than these shall he do. —*John 14:12.*

We consecrate our lives to the unfoldment and expression of the divine sonship, so that we may fulfill His life in ours.

I am the light of the world: he that followeth me shall not walk in the darkness, but shall have the light of life.—*John 8:12.*

We turn from the darkness of limitation to the eternal light of the Christ; from the belief in evil and depravity to the truth of the all-infolding good.

I came that they may have life, and may have *it* abundantly.—*John 10:10.*

My life, my health, my joy, my supply, are of God. I am one with Him, and all that He has is mine.

Every good gift and every perfect gift is from above, coming down from the Father of lights, with whom can be no variation, neither shadow that is cast by turning.—*James 1:17.*

*Glory to God in the highest,
And on earth peace among men in
    whom he is well pleased.*
          —Luke 2:14.

312   Easter

I am the resurrection, and the life: he that believeth on me, though he die, yet shall he live and whosoever liveth and believeth on me shall never die.—*John 11:25.*

Know ye not, that to whom ye present yourselves as servants unto obedience, his servants ye are whom ye obey; whether of sin unto death, or of obedience unto righteousness? —Rom. 6:16.

Being made free from sin, and become servants to God, ye have your fruit unto sanctification, and the end eternal life.—*Rom. 6:22.*

The law of the Spirit of life in Christ Jesus made me free from the law of sin and of death.—Rom. 8:2.

The Spirit himself beareth witness with our spirit, that we are children of God: and if children, then heirs; heirs of God, and joint-heirs with Christ.—*Rom. 8:16, 17.*

For I am persuaded, that neither death, nor life, nor angels, nor principalities, nor things present, nor things to come, nor powers, nor height, nor depth, nor any other creature, shall be able to separate us from the love of God, which is in Christ Jesus our Lord.—Rom. 8:38, 39.

The first man is of the earth, earthy: the second man is of heaven. —*I Cor. 15:47.*

And as we have borne the image of the earthly, we shall also bear the image of the heavenly.—I Cor. 15:49.

When this corruptible shall have put on incorruption, and this mortal shall have put on immortality, then shall come to pass the saying that is written, Death is swallowed up in victory.—*I Cor. 15:54.*

Thanks be to God, who giveth us the victory through our Lord Jesus Christ.—I Cor. 15:57.

313 Healing

Thou stretchest forth thy hand to heal.—*Acts 4:30.*

Heal the sick . . . and say unto them, Thy kingdom of God is come nigh unto you.—Luke 10:9.

My help *cometh* from Jehovah, who made heaven and earth.—*Psalms 121: 2.*

The prayer of faith shall save him that is sick, and the Lord shall raise him up.—James 5:15.

I am Jehovah that healeth thee. —*Exod. 15:26.*

Why art thou cast down, O my soul? And why art thou disquieted within me? Hope thou in God; for I shall yet praise him, who is the help of my countenance, and my God. —Psalms 42:11.

He healeth the broken in heart, and bindeth up their wounds.—*Psalms 147:3.*

The Spirit of the Lord is upon me, because he anointed me to preach good tidings to the poor: he hath sent me to proclaim release to the captives, and recovering of sight to the blind, to set at liberty them that are bruised, to proclaim the acceptable year of the Lord.—Luke 4:18.

Unto you that fear my name shall the sun of righteousness arise with healing in its wings.—*Mal. 4:2.*

There shall no evil befall thee, neither shall any plague come nigh thy tent.—Psalms 91:10.

When thou passest through the waters, I will be with thee; and through the rivers, they shall not overflow thee: when thou walkest through the fire, thou shalt not be burned, neither shall the flame kindle upon thee.—*Isa. 43:2.*

And all things, whatsoever ye shall ask in prayer, believing, ye shall receive.—Matt. 21:22.

314 Healing

And Jesus went about all the cities and the villages, teaching in their synagogues, and preaching the gospel of the kingdom, and healing all manner of disease and all manner of sickness. —*Matt. 9:35.*

And many followed him; and he healed them all.—Matt. 12:15.

And Jesus . . . called them, and said, What will ye that I should do unto you?—*Matt. 20:32.*

They say unto him, Lord, that our eyes may be opened. . . . And straightway they received their sight.—Matt. 20:33, 34.

Then shall thy light break forth as the morning, and thy healing shall spring forth speedily.—*Isa. 58:8.*

I will take sickness away from the midst of thee.—Exod. 23:25.

Behold, I will heal thee . . . And I will add unto thy days.—*II Kings 20:5, 6.*

Heal me, O Jehovah, and I shall be healed; save me, and I shall be saved: for thou art my praise.—Jer. 17:14.

Behold, I will bring . . . health and cure, and I will cure them; and I will reveal unto them abundance of peace and truth.—*Jer. 33:6.*

He will heal us . . . he will raise us up, and we shall live before him. —Hosea 6:1, 2.

Unto you that fear my name shall the sun of righteousness arise with healing in its wings.—*Mal. 4:2.*

The prayer of faith shall save him that is sick, and the Lord shall raise him up.—James 5:15.

315   Mother's Day

Honor thy father and thy mother. —*Exod. 20:12.*

God has chosen my mother for me

and through her God guides and directs my way.

As one whom his mother comforteth, so will I comfort you.—*Isa. 66: 13.*

Through the love, comfort, and kindness of my mother I can understand the loving-kindness of God.

He that loveth father or mother more than me is not worthy of me; and he that loveth son or daughter more than me is not worthy of me. —*Matt. 10:37.*

One is the Father of all. My mother and father and all of my family are dearer to me because I know that we are all children of God, who is Father of all.

And his mother kept all these sayings in her heart.—*Luke 2:51.*

As Mary, the mother of Jesus, helped Him to grow and to know the Christ Spirit within Him, so my mother helps me to grow and to bring forth all that is best within me.

Whosoever would be first among you shall be your servant.—*Matt. 20:27.*

This is Mother's Day. Mother has earned first place by giving the most loving, unselfish service.

316   New Year's Day

In the beginning God created the heavens and the earth. . . . And God saw everything that he had made, and, behold, it was very good.—*Gen. 1:1, 31.*

The heavens declare the glory of God; and the firmament showeth his handiwork.—Psalms 19:1.

Let all the earth fear Jehovah: let all the inhabitants of the world stand in awe of him. For he spake, and it was done; he commanded, and it stood fast.—*Psalms 33:8, 9.*

The heavens are thine, the earth also is thine: the world and the fulness thereof, thou hast founded them. —Psalms 89:11.

Before the mountains were brought forth, or ever thou hadst formed the earth and the world, even from everlasting to everlasting, thou art God. —*Psalms 90:2.*

Know ye that Jehovah, he is God: it is he that hath made us, and we are his; we are his people, and the sheep of his pasture.—Psalms 100:3.

I know that, whatsoever God doeth, it shall be for ever: nothing can be put to it, nor anything taken from it . . . That which is hath been long ago; and that which is to be hath long ago been: and God seeking again that which is passed away.—*Eccl. 3:14, 15.*

How great are his signs! and how mighty are his wonders! his kingdom is an everlasting kingdom, and his dominion is from generation to generation.—Dan. 4:3.

Am I a God at hand, saith Jehovah, and not a God afar off? Can any hide himself in secret places so that I shall not see him? . . . Do not I fill heaven and earth? saith Jehovah.—*Jer. 23:23, 24.*

Look unto me, and be ye saved, all the ends of the earth; for I am God, and there is none else.—Isa. 45:22.

317   Prosperity

Believe in Jehovah your God, so shall ye be established . . . so shall ye prosper.—*II Chron. 20:20.*

The God of heaven, he will prosper us; therefore we his servants will arise and build.—Neh. 2:20.

They shall prosper that love thee. —*Psalms 122:6.*

In nothing be anxious; but in everything by prayer and supplication with thanksgiving let your requests be made known unto God. And the peace of God, which passeth all understanding, shall guard your hearts and your thoughts.—Phil. 4:6, 7.

If they hearken and serve him, they shall spend their days in prosperity.—*Job 36:11.*

For unto every one that hath shall be given, and he shall have abundance: but from him that hath not, even that which he hath shall be taken away.—Matt. 25:29.

By thy wisdom and by thine understanding thou hast gotten thee riches, and hast gotten gold and silver into thy treasures.—*Ezek. 28:4.*

I will be with thee; I will not fail thee, nor forsake thee.—Josh. 1:5.

The proving of your faith worketh patience. And let patience have *its* perfect work, that ye may be perfect and entire, lacking in nothing.—*James 1:3, 4.*

And . . . God shall supply every need of yours, according to his riches in glory in Christ Jesus.—Phil. 4:19.

318   Prosperity

I will stand upon my watch, and set me upon the tower, and will look forth to see what he will speak with me. —*Hab. 2:1.*

If I have the gift of prophecy, and know all mysteries and all knowledge; and if I have all faith, so as to remove mountains, but have not love, I am nothing.—I Cor. 13:2.

Christ liveth in me: and that life which I now live in the flesh I live in faith, the faith which is in the Son of God.—*Gal. 2:20.*

For in Christ Jesus neither . . . availeth anything . . . but faith working through love.—*Gal. 5:6.*

I know thy works, and thy love and faith and ministry and patience, and that thy last works are more than the first.—*Rev. 2:19.*

Both riches and honor come of thee, and thou rulest over all; and in thy hand is power and might; and in thy hand it is to make great, and to give strength unto all.—I Chron. 29:12.

Christ . . . dwell in your hearts through faith; to the end that ye, being rooted and grounded in love . . . know the love of Christ which passeth knowledge.—*Eph. 3:17, 19.*

Let us draw near with a true heart in fulness of faith.—Heb. 10:22.

By faith we understand that the worlds have been framed by the word of God.—*Heb. 11:3.*

Be sober, be watchful . . . stedfast in your faith . . . And the God of all grace . . . shall himself perfect, establish, strengthen you.—I Peter 5:8, 10.

319   Sunday School

God is my kind and loving Father. I am His obedient child.

God is life and health, radiant, glowing, perfect.

I picture the health of God in my mind and in my body.

God is love, and His love fills my heart and my life.

I show forth the love of God to all that I meet.

God is joy and light, and His brightness shines in all the earth.

I find my true happiness in the light of God.

God is substance, and there is abundance of all good for all people.

I see God in all things and I rejoice in the realization of plenty.

God is harmony, and His lovingkindness is everywhere.

I live in peace and harmony with all His children.

God is wisdom and knows all things.

I am wise with the wisdom of God.

God is freedom, and His perfect liberty is for all.

I am free in the knowledge that I am God's child.

God is mind, and all His ideas are good.

I let the mind of God work through me in all that I do, and think good thoughts after Him.

God is Truth, and He is forever the same, yesterday, today, and forever.

I find the real and the true by keeping close to God in all my ways.

320   Thanksgiving Day

God give thee of the dew of heaven, and of the fatness of the earth, and plenty of grain and new wine.—*Gen. 27:28.*

He that supplieth seed to the sower and bread for food, shall supply and multiply your seed for sowing, and increase the fruits of your righteousness: ye being enriched in everything unto all liberality, which worketh through us thanksgiving to God.—II Cor. 9:10, 11.

Behold, the days come, saith Jehovah, that the plowman shall overtake the reaper, and the treader of grapes him that soweth seed; and the mountains shall drop sweet wine, and all the hills shall melt.—*Amos 9:13.*

And ye shall eat in plenty and be satisfied, and shall praise the name of Jehovah your God, that hath dealt wondrously with you.—Joel 2:26.

Jehovah hath comforted Zion; he hath comforted all her waste places, and hath made her wilderness like Eden, and her desert like the garden of Jehovah; joy and gladness shall be found therein, thanksgiving, and the voice of melody.—*Isa. 51:3.*

Saith Jehovah, Stand ye in the ways and see, and ask for the old paths, where is the good way; and walk therein, and ye shall find rest for your souls.—Jer. 6:16.

Except Jehovah build the house, they labor in vain that build it: except Jehovah keep the city, the watchman waketh but in vain.—*Psalms 127:1.*

Wisdom is as good as an inheritance; yea, more excellent is it for them that see the sun. For wisdom is a defence, even as money is a defence; but the excellency of knowledge is, that wisdom preserveth the life of him that hath it.—Eccl. 7:11, 12.

Make the voice of thanksgiving to be heard, and tell of all thy wondrous works.—*Psalms 26:7.*

Give thanks unto the name of Jehovah. . . . For . . . they shall prosper that love thee.—Psalms 122:4, 6.

The simple form of spiritual baptism given here is used at Unity Chapel in Kansas City the fourth Sunday of each month in connection with the induction of new members. The speaker announces that new members are to be received and invites them, as the chairmen reads their names, to come forward and stand facing him to receive spiritual baptism. The speaker briefly welcomes them into membership in Unity Society, concluding his remarks as follows:

"In Unity we do not make use of water in baptism, as did John of old, but prefer instead to follow the example of Jesus, whose form of baptism John foretold (Mark 1:7, 8): 'There cometh after me he that is mightier than I, the latchet of whose shoes I am not worthy to stoop down and unloose. I baptized you in water; but he shall baptize you in the Holy Spirit.'

"The account of Jesus' baptism of His disciples is found in the 20th chapter of the Gospel of John, verses 19 and 22: 'When therefore it was evening, on that day, the first *day* of the week, and when the doors were shut where the disciples were, for fear of the Jews, Jesus came and stood in the midst, and saith unto them, Peace *be* unto you. And when he had said this, he showed unto them his hands and his side. The disciples therefore were glad, when they saw the Lord. Jesus therefore said to them again, Peace *be* unto you: as the Father hath sent me, even so send I you. And when he had said this, he breathed on them, and saith unto them, Receive ye the Holy Spirit.'

"So, in His blessed name, we invite you to receive that Holy Spirit. Will the congregation kindly rise, and repeat for these our new members, this charge:

"In the name and through the power of Jesus Christ, receive ye the Holy Spirit.

"Let us repeat the statement first aloud and then silently, three times."

The music of hymn Number 295 is played softly while the speaker leads the congregation in repeating the blessing. Then the soloist or choir sings the words of the hymn while the speaker, new members, and congregation stand silent. At the conclusion of the hymn the speaker says, "Amen," and the new members and the congregation are seated.

322   Offertory

Divine love through me blesses and multiplies this offering. (Repeat this three times—in the name of the Father, in the name of the Son, and in the name of the Holy Spirit.)

323   Benediction

May the Lord watch between thee and me, and make us know that we are all one in Spirit.

INDEX

Titles are listed in roman type, first lines that differ from titles are in italics.

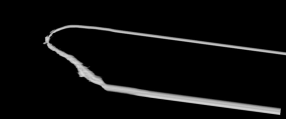

TOPICAL INDEX

Only titles are listed

Omnipresence

Patriotic

Peace

Praise

Prayer

Prosperity

Response

49
177
204
90

PRINTED U.S.A.

14C-12M-2-65